Baker, Nina (Brown)
Henry Hudson

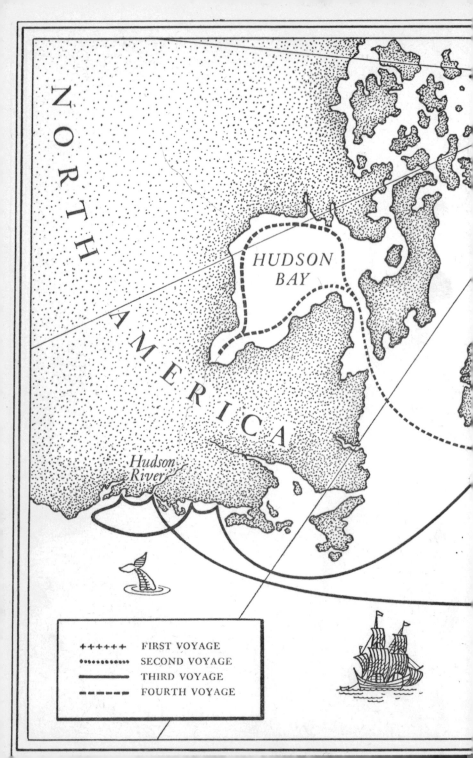

NORTH AMERICA

HUDSON BAY

Hudson River

++++++ FIRST VOYAGE
•••••••••• SECOND VOYAGE
———— THIRD VOYAGE
- - - - FOURTH VOYAGE

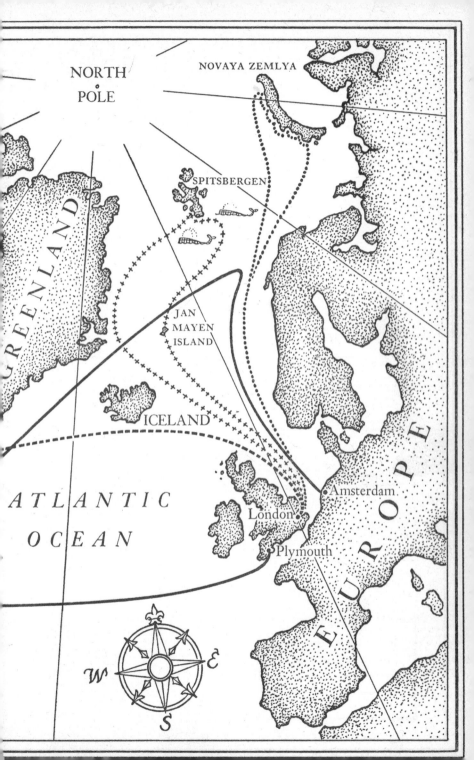

BOOKS BY

Nina Brown Baker

AMERIGO VESPUCCI

JUAN PONCE DE LEON

HENRY HUDSON

These are Borzoi Books
PUBLISHED IN NEW YORK BY
ALFRED · A · KNOPF

Henry Hudson

HENRY HUDSON

by Nina Brown Baker

ILLUSTRATED BY GEORGE FULTON

New York *Alfred A Knopf* 1958

L. C. catalog card number: 58-5356

© Nina Sydney Ladof

THIS IS A BORZOI BOOK,
PUBLISHED BY ALFRED A. KNOPF, INC.

FIRST EDITION

For Patricia Drew

Foreword

Hudson, Henry, a distinguished English navigator of whose personal history before April 19, 1607, or after June 21, 1611, *absolutely nothing is known. . . .*
—Encyclopædia Britannica

most *biographies tell us when and where the hero was born, and something of his early days. In the case of Captain Henry Hudson, this is impossible. All that is known of him concerns his last four voyages. His story begins in mystery and ends in mystery. Yet into four short years he crowded the excitement and adventure of a lifetime. And, in one of those years, he won the fame which has endured for more than three centuries.*

Contents

Henry Hudson

Captain Hudson's First Chance

WARM at the North Pole? Warmer than England?" The oldest director spoke fretfully. "How can that be, Master Hudson? I've always heard the Pole was the coldest place on earth. Anyway, no one has ever been there. How can you know what the climate is?"

Captain Henry Hudson sighed. He had stood before the Board for an hour, carefully explaining. It would be possible to reach China from England by sailing north, directly across the North Pole. This was the shortest route. No one had ever tried it before. If the Muscovy Company would back him, he was sure he could manage it.

The other directors had seemed to be impressed. But the old man, napping in his armchair, must have missed it all. Carefully Hudson began all over again, addressing him directly.

"My lord, the sun does not set at the North Pole for half the year. Now, your lordship knows how it is in heating a room. A small fire, never allowed to go out, does better than a big one which dies at night and must be rekindled every morning. The constant heat keeps some warmth in walls and floor. So it is at the Pole. The land and water, continuously soaked in sunshine, will store warmth and preserve it."

The old man looked doubtful, and Hudson hurried on.

"I do not present this notion as my own, your lordship. I have here some letters from the famous Dutch geographer, Peter Plancius. He advances the idea with many learned arguments. I have not troubled the Company with them. Shall I read them to you?"

He picked up a thick roll of parchment, but the old man waved it away.

"No, no, I wouldn't dispute an authority like Plancius. He says it's warm up there, does he? But how about all that ice?"

The other directors exchanged impatient glances. But Hudson spoke patiently.

"The ice is merely a fringe which must be broken through. Once that is done, the air will grow warmer and warmer as we approach the Pole. Not only Plancius, but the Reverend Samuel Purchas and many other scholars agree on this. I have documents here—"

The chairman of the Company, a younger man, interrupted hastily.

"It will not be necessary to read them, Captain Hudson. We are businessmen, not scholars. Our only interest is to find a short sea route to the Eastern lands. You say it can be done by sailing north, over the Pole."

"I am sure it can be done in that way," Hudson said firmly. "All I ask is a chance to prove it."

"Well—" The chairman glanced around the table. There were some eight or ten men there, prosperous merchants in fur-trimmed robes and gold chains.

"I think we might take a vote," the chairman went on. "I, for one, am convinced that Master Hudson can do what he promises. I vote for giving him the ship and men he wants. What is your pleasure, gentlemen?

One by one they agreed. Even the oldest director produced a grumbling: "Oh, let him try it. But it still sounds silly to me. Warm at the North Pole!"

The meeting settled down then to a discussion of ways and means. Hudson was to have a ship, the *Hopewell*, and a crew of ten men. All expenses were to be borne by the Company. Hudson himself would have his pay as ship's master, and no more. The Company would take all profits. Hudson was dismissed, with orders to return next day, when the contract would be ready for signing.

The fresh March air was a relief after the stuffy smell of the warehouse office. Hudson went outside, and paused a minute in the cobbled yard.

The yard led directly onto the dock, where one of the Company's ships was unloading. Wine from Portugal, to judge from the big barrels being rolled down the rough planks. Hudson himself had made the dull voyage to Portugal and back many times. He smiled now to think that he need not do it again. This time, something far more adventurous lay ahead.

He passed through the yard gate, to be greeted by an excited cry of: "Father! Is it all right? Did they say Yes?"

Hudson tried to look stern. "You waited all this time, John? You should have gone back, as I told you. Mother will scold you for being late to supper."

"Now she can scold both of us!" The boy laughed. "I had to know, Father. What did the gentlemen say? Will they let you sail north to China?"

"Come along. I'll tell you as we go."

Father and son set off along the narrow dockside street. Their home lay to the east, through the twisting alleys of London's Billingsgate section.

Captain Hudson walked rapidly, with long, impatient strides. Young John, breathless from trying to keep up, urged: "You haven't told me yet, Father."

"Then I'll tell you now, John. The answer was Yes. At first I thought there wasn't a chance. I'd never have persuaded them if it hadn't been for one thing. They were struck by my argument that it must be warm at the North Pole. Once I drove that home, they were willing to agree to my plan. And they did agree. They're giving me a ship to find the northern passage. Right over the Pole, and down the Russian coast to China."

"Just what you wanted! Oh, Father, it's wonderful! I'm so glad." Then the boy's glowing face turned thoughtful. "You're sure it *is*, aren't you? Warm at the North Pole?"

"Who knows?" A deep laugh rumbled from the Captain's chest. "And for that matter, who cares? Dr. Plancius and the other learned men say it must be. If they're right, so much the better. But *I'm* not asking for warm weather. If I have to battle cold, I'll battle it, as I did on my voyages to Norway. I'm used to cold. It has no terrors for me."

"Nor me," John said valiantly. "I don't mind being cold, not ever. Father—you'll take me with

you, won't you? You promised I could sail with you when I was old enough. I'm past twelve now, and I've never been to sea yet. You took Oliver all the way to Venice last year."

"Perhaps I should take your brother Oliver this time," Captain Hudson said teasingly. "He's grown up, and might be more useful."

"He'd be no use at all," John declared. "Oliver hates the sea. He likes working for the butcher. Besides, he's just been married. You know his wife wouldn't let him go. And I *could* be useful. You'll have to have a cabin boy. I'd be a better cabin boy than anyone you've ever had. Oh, Father, please, please let me go!"

Hudson looked down into the eager blue eyes, so like his own. Just so he had waited, holding his breath, for the directors to give him the answer he hoped for. His consent now meant as much to the boy as theirs had meant to him.

"We'll have to ask your mother," he warned. "But if she agrees, I won't say No."

John hurried his steps to a run. He had already reached home and blurted out the news when his father entered.

"Now, now, wait and let Father tell me," Mrs. Hudson said. She turned from the fire to greet her husband with a smile. "Is it good news then, love?"

"The best." Captain Hudson kissed her cheek and picked up a small boy playing on the floor.

"Well, Richard! Starving, are you?" He set the baby on a high stool at the table and pulled out a chair for himself.

The wife brought a huge bowl of fish stew from the fireplace. John passed around smaller bowls and his father ladled out the stew. This, with a loaf of black bread, was their evening meal.

John and his mother took their places. The boy waited impatiently as Captain Hudson asked the blessing. Then he broke out: "Father and I are going to sail over the North Pole, Mother! And we don't care if it's hot or cold, just so we find a way to China. We can do it, too. We know we can."

"Not so much of the 'we,' son," Captain Hudson interrupted. "I told you you'd have to get your mother's permission."

Mrs. Hudson hesitated a minute. Then she smiled.

"The captain chooses the crew, as everyone

knows. If your father has chosen you, John, it is not for me to object. And now, my boy, eat your supper and keep quiet."

She turned to her husband.

"I knew this meeting was very important to you, my dear. For weeks I've seen you bent over your maps, writing long letters to Dr. Plancius, studying his replies. But you haven't said much, and I didn't like to bother you with questions. Now that it's all settled, perhaps you're ready to tell me more."

He squeezed her hand gratefully. "I'm ready to tell you everything, Kate. It's true I haven't talked much about this plan. I was afraid to, for fear it would come to nothing. But now— Oh, I'll wear you out with talking!"

He paused, and then went on a little shame-facedly: "Perhaps it's foolish for a forty-year-old man to be so excited over this. But it's what I've wanted all my life. When I was a boy, I used to listen to tales of Christopher Columbus, and Vespucci, and our own John Cabot. I wanted to do what they had done—push off into unknown seas, find new waters that do not show on any map."

"And yet you wouldn't go to Virginia, when Captain John Smith asked you," Mrs. Hudson remarked. "I thought you seemed regretful, when you came back from seeing him off last December."

"I did have some regrets," he admitted. "But after all, Virginia is known. Smith wasn't going exploring. He was going to found an English colony there. I don't want to found colonies. I want to explore the unknown! It's what I've always dreamed of. That's why I chose the sea in the first place. And now, after all the long waiting, my dream has come true."

"Long waiting indeed," his wife said gently. "I'm afraid I'm to blame for that, Henry. You had to make a living for me and the children. For years you've journeyed from one well-known port to another, earning our daily bread. And yet you never complained."

"I had nothing to complain of," he answered. "These tame, breadwinning voyages have taught me my trade. And not for anything would I have missed our happy home, and you, and the children. Oh, no! I haven't even been impatient. I knew that in God's good time, my chance would come. And now, praise be to God, it has come at last!"

To the Far North

LIKE Columbus, Henry Hudson was an earnest
student of geography.

At this time—1607—scholars knew far more
than they had known in Columbus's day. No one
now doubted that the earth was round. To reach
the East by sailing west was perfectly possible. Indeed, Magellan's expedition had done it in the early
1520's.

Magellan's route was not a good one. The American continents, North and South, were in the way. Magellan had to go down to the tip of South America and around it. This was such a long and difficult route that no one used it. Hudson's idea was to find a shorter way by sailing first north, over the Pole, and then south.

Hudson's geography, like that of Columbus, had some holes in it. Columbus did not know about America. Hudson did not know about Siberia. Although European Russia was on the map, Asiatic Russia was not. Hudson thought that he had only to round the Scandinavian peninsula, skirt Russia's northern shore, and then turn south to China.

Columbus was wrong. Henry Hudson was wrong. And a good thing, too. Without these wrong notions, both men would have stayed at home, and history would be very different. The old director who couldn't believe it was warm at the North Pole was right. And who even knows his name? Sometimes the right kind of wrongness is better than the wrong kind of rightness.

Hudson hoped that the learned men were right when they talked about the warm North Pole. But he could not see that it really mattered much, one way or another. He had made voyages to Norway. He had dodged the ice floes of the lower Norwegian Sea. If there were bigger ones as he sailed north, he thought he could dodge them, too. It would not be for long. Once he turned the corner of Russia and headed south, those difficulties would be over.

So, with his head full of wrong notions, and well supplied with faulty maps, Henry Hudson began to get his expedition together.

The Muscovy Company provided the ship, a sturdy square-rigged craft of eighty tons. It was stocked with food and drink for a six-month voyage.

The food would seem pretty dreadful to a modern seaman. It consisted of sea biscuit (dry bread baked in loaves as hard as brick and not much tastier), salt beef, salt pork, and salt fish, cheese, olive oil or butter, and dried peas. There was plenty of beer to wash it down—a gallon a day to each man.

If the food was rough, living accommodations aboard ship were even more so. The captain and mate shared a tiny cramped cabin. This at least had built-in bunks, although the cabin boy slept on the floor.

The forecastle, the men's quarters, was pretty well jammed with ropes and spare gear. The sailors slung their hammocks there, in what space they could find. For chairs they used a coil of rope or a keg of salt fish. Food was cooked on the open deck, over a charcoal fire laid on an iron plate.

Larger ships carried a cook, but the little *Hopewell* did not. Besides captain and mate, there were only ten men and a boy in the crew. Any man off duty in the early morning would light the cooking fire, put the pot on to boil, and drop in the salt meat and peas. It boiled all day, and the men helped themselves as they came off watch. They ate squatting on deck, from wooden trenchers. Dishwashing was nobody's job, and it is not likely that the trenchers were ever cleaned.

The officers fared a little better, but not much. Their food was brought to the cabin by the boy, who also had the job of keeping the cabin clean and doing the officers' laundry.

In this little world of a ship at sea, the captain was king. He could have the slightest disobedience punished by flogging, or by whatever punishment he thought would teach the culprit a lesson. Some captains were very ingenious with these punishments.

A favorite one was to toss the wrongdoer overboard and tow him behind the ship until cold sea water brought repentance.

For the really serious offenses, the captain could inflict the death penalty at his pleasure. Many a ship came home with a crewman missing and the brief entry in the ship's log: "Hanged at the yardarm for insubordination." The authorities ashore demanded only that every disciplinary act, whether trifling or extreme, be properly entered on the books.

Such power, in the hands of a brutal captain, could easily be abused, and it often was. The best of captains found it useful to have, even if they used it sparingly. Seamen of those days were a tough lot, and discipline must be maintained.

In his earlier voyages, Captain Henry Hudson had had no trouble with his men. Most of the trips had been short runs to European trading ports. The sailors had a chance to add to their wages by doing a little trading on their own. They could bring along their private stock of English tinware and sell it in Amsterdam or Genoa, investing the proceeds in Dutch cheese or Italian leather goods. This business opportunity attracted the best type of seamen; thrifty, sensible men who were interested in seeing that the voyage went smoothly.

Captain Hudson had something of a shock when he began recruiting a crew for the Arctic venture. His former sailors could see that a trading voyage to China would be very profitable. But who knew if they would ever reach China?

It was hard enough to get to Archangel, the Russian port where the Muscovy Company did business. This connection had been set up some years before, under the direction of Sebastian Cabot. "Muscovy" is the old name for Russia. The Muscovy Company had some trade in Chinese goods bought from the Russians. Now they hoped to extend it by sending Hudson to China itself.

All this Captain Hudson patiently explained to the men he hoped to hire. Some of them had been to Archangel. They remembered the floating ice and bitter cold of the northern seas. It was bad enough when you hugged the Norwegian coast, as their ships had done. Farther north, straight to the

Pole—oh, no, thanks. Scholars might believe that the climate grew warmer as you sailed north. The sailors did not believe it. They were not willing to risk their lives to find out.

Hudson had better luck in choosing his mate. John Colman had sailed with him before. He was a slow, plodding man, not too intelligent, but honest and loyal.

"If it's good enough for you, Cap'n, it's good enough for me," he said. "But you might as well make up your mind to put up with a scratch crew. The old hands won't touch it. You'll have to make do with riffraff. Poachers and petty thieves you'll get, just ahead of the law. Worthless sons and shiftless husbands. And, of course, the gamblers who hope to get rich by cheating the heathen. That's the kind of crew you'll get, Cap'n. You might as well make up your mind to it."

"I'm afraid you're right," Hudson answered. "So long as they can sail a ship, I won't ask too many questions. Come with me on a tour of the dockside taverns. You can help me choose the best of the worst, anyway."

They rounded up ten men. All that could be said for them was that they were experienced sailors. Some were drunk. Most bore the black eyes and bruises of tavern brawls. All, of course, were penniless. Those who had any of last voyage's wages left laughed at the idea of signing on until it was gone.

Captain Hudson did what he could. He saw that plenty of food and beer was provided, and of good quality. He divided duties fairly, so that each man would have no more than his share. He hoped that, given no grounds for complaint, the crew would do well enough.

On Sunday, April 19, 1607, he led them all to the church of St. Ethelburga for a last Communion service. Hudson himself was a devoutly religious man. It is not likely that religion meant much to the gang of ruffians who shuffled into church after him. But regulations provided that the captain look after his men's souls as well as their bodies. Aboard ship, he would be their pastor, holding regular Sabbath services. In case of death at sea, the captain would conduct funeral rites from the English Book of Common Prayer.

The men had sobered up and cleaned up for the service at St. Ethelburga's. They behaved well enough, standing and kneeling at the proper times, joining lustily in the hymns. Looking them over throughout the long service, the Captain felt his heart lighten. A scratch crew, as Colman had said. But he thought he could manage with them.

Once outside the church, the men scattered quickly. Hudson lingered on the steps for a minute with his son John and the mate Colman.

"They're in a hurry to get home to their dinners," John observed as the last man disappeared from sight.

Colman laughed. "It's not dinner they have in mind, Master John. Off to the nearest alehouse, that's what they are. It'll take a quart apiece to wash the taste of the hymns out of their throats. I must say though, Cap'n, they did us proud. Put their pennies in the offering, every man of 'em. And I didn't see a single hand take a fistful out. Of course, they knew I'd be watching. I warned them I would."

"Oh, come now, Colman, they're not so bad as all that." Captain Hudson laughed. "I thought myself they behaved very well. Better than our cabin boy here did," he added severely. "I've told you before, John, you must sit still and not fidget during the sermon."

"I didn't mean to fidget," the boy said. "It's just that I can't sit still anywhere, Father. I'm too excited! I start thinking about where we're going, and all the strange things we're going to see. I just can't wait. Don't you know yet when we start, Father? Do you think it will be tomorrow?"

"No, it will not be tomorrow. And no, I don't know exactly what day we'll get off. The ship isn't half loaded yet. And it won't be, until the directors make up their minds what they want to send. Each of the gentlemen has his own ideas of what the Chinese people might buy. That's the Company's business, John, not ours. But they tell me it won't be very long."

"How long?" the boy persisted. "A week? A month? I don't think I can wait a whole month!"

"Then you'll never make a sailor, Master John," Colman told him. "Wait for the wind, wait for the tide, wait for the storm to wear itself out, wait for orders— Oh, a sailor's life is made up of waiting. You might as well start practicing patience now, boy. It's one thing every sailorman has to learn. Cap'n here will tell you the same."

Hudson smiled down at his son. "Indeed I will, John. You've never been a patient boy, have you?

Maybe you'd better start practicing patience now. That will give you something to do until sailing day."

"Yes, I will," John said earnestly. "I'm already practicing cabin work—carrying trays and making beds and washing shirts. Mother says I'm doing very well—turning into a regular little housemaid, she says. Now I'll try being patient. But it's going to be harder."

John had thirteen days to practice patience. The *Hopewell* sailed on May Day. Mrs. Hudson and little Richard came down to St. Katherine's Docks to see them off, along with the older son Oliver and his bride. So did a crowd of other women—the mothers, wives, and sweethearts of the crew.

Tearful farewells were exchanged. The men went aboard. Captain Hudson took his place and gave the final orders. The mainsail rose to a hearty chant:

> *"Yo ho, raise her, Ned,*
> *Yo ho ho!"*

Lines were cast off, and the *Hopewell* moved slowly down Thames River, bound for China by way of the Far North.

The Wall of Ice

FAIR winds sped the *Hopewell* up the English Channel and along the coast of northern England and Scotland. Heading steadily northward, they had their first sight of Greenland in June.

This was not a new discovery. Other northern voyagers had seen the mountainous island and marked it on their maps. Hudson had all the available maps with him. They differed from each other, and not one was accurate. Greenland turned up on them as Greenland, Groenland, Engroenland, and Grocland.

Hudson, making his own map from what he saw, added to the confusion by giving new names to certain points. He called one region "Hold-with-Hope," and a mountain "Mount of God's Mercie."

The names may have had a meaning which is not clear to us. It was off Greenland that the voyage first fell into difficulties. Hudson spent over two weeks in sight of Hold-with-Hope, vainly battling the strong Greenland Current which kept him back from his northern course. It must have taken all the hope he could muster to hold against that current. Perhaps he felt that it was only by God's mercy that he finally worked as far north as the bleak rock mountain.

Off Mount of God's Mercie they ran into a wall of ice, stretching from west to east. In midsummer it would begin to melt, breaking up into separate icebergs slowly drifting south. But now in June it was still as solid as stone.

Unless he could find a gap in the ice wall, Hudson's plan to sail to the Pole was hopeless. The ship lay to for a few days, waiting for the Captain to decide what to do next.

Young John came to his father as he sat in his cabin, frowning over the maps. He came timidly, with a request to pass on.

"The men told me to ask you, Father. They say they're getting good and sick being aboard all this time. As long as we're idle here, they want to know if some of them can take a boat and go ashore."

Captain Hudson's frown deepened. "Go ashore? What for? There's nothing there but rocks and mountains and ice. No people, and no alehouses, if that's what they hope for. And no proper landing place that I can see, even for a small boat. What put this idiotic notion into their heads?"

"Well, they thought they might look for oyster beds," John explained. "James Young sailed to the Indies once with the Spanish. He said they found pearl oysters on just such a rocky coast."

"Pearl oysters in the Arctic!" Captain Hudson snorted. "Surely the most ignorant of them must know better than that."

"I don't think they really expect pearls," John admitted. "It's just that they're getting restless, being cooped up on the ship so long. It wouldn't hurt to let them go, would it, Father?"

"It wouldn't help," Captain Hudson said curtly. "There'll be plenty of work to keep them busy once we get under way again." He looked back at his charts and sighed. "So far as I can see, we'll have to turn east and sail along the ice wall until we find an opening. It will take us leagues out of our way, but there's nothing else to do."

"It seems a shame to leave Greenland without exploring it at all," John ventured.

Captain Hudson laid down his pen.

"See here, boy," he said sternly. "The Muscovy Company did not hire me to explore Greenland. I undertook to find a passage to China. We are here to explore the waterways, not the barren lands where the Company could do no business. The men are too ignorant to understand this. But I had expected better of my son. Do you understand now?"

"Yes, sir," the boy answered. He turned away, and then turned back. "Shall I try to explain it to the men, Father?"

"You'd be wasting your time," Hudson said

wearily. "Tell them simply this. Say that the Captain said: 'Permission refused.' That's all they need to know."

Perhaps it was. It would have been enough for well-trained men accustomed to accepting their captain's orders with no reason given. Captain Hudson failed to allow for the fact that he was not dealing with men of that type. He would have been wiser to humor their natural desire to stretch their legs ashore, even though no useful purpose was served.

No particular harm came from this incident. But it shows the sort of mistake that Henry Hudson was to make over and over again. As he had told John, he himself was a sea explorer. What he wanted was to find a sea road to the East. He cared nothing at all for the lands which lay along that road. He did not see why anyone else should care. "Sail on, sail on!" was supposed to have been the motto of Admiral Columbus. It was certainly Henry Hudson's.

As soon as the wind favored him, he turned eastward, following the ice wall. It was a jagged line, with deep notches which looked like openings. But always the open water narrowed to nothing, and the ice barrier stretched unbroken.

Hudson had spoken lightly of the "fringe of ice" which surrounded the Pole. He had expected to force a way through it into the open polar waters. Warm waters they would be. Or so the scholars had assured him. They might have been boiling hot, for all the good it did him. The ice wall lay between, as solid as stone, and there was no way through it.

Hudson was a stubborn man, and he hated to give up. There *must* be a way through the ice, if only he could find it! He spent nearly all of June patiently prodding for an opening. Then, on June 27, the ice gave way to land. He had reached the island of Spitsbergen, lying north of Norway.

Spitsbergen, discovered earlier by the Dutchman Willem Barents, was on the maps. Hudson had no more interest in it than he had had in Greenland. He noted in his journal the great number of whales seen in its coastal waters. Nothing could have seemed less important to him than the presence of these great sea creatures. He could not know that, to his employers, this would be the only useful result of his voyage.

Hudson did not care about whales, and he did not care about Spitsbergen. The island blocked his path, as the ice wall had done. He must find a way around it. He spent an exhausting month trying, and failed completely. Where the land left off, the ice began again.

And now, in July, the ice became a dangerous enemy. It was no longer a solid wall, harmless if he kept far enough away. The Arctic sun shone down twenty-four hours a day. Under its rays, the ice started to melt in the cracks. Huge towering pieces broke off and began to drift southward.

It was just such a floating ice mountain that wrecked the mighty modern steamer *Titanic*. The little *Hopewell* would have had no chance against one of them. Hudson needed all his seamanship to keep out of their paths. He was further harassed by violent gales of wind and by rain and fog. The Captain grew worried and short tempered. The men grumbled and complained constantly. Even little John began to wonder why he had ever thought that exploring was fun.

Fleeing from one storm, the ship put into a bay

on Spitsbergen's south coast. The water here was calm and swarming with whales. The creatures were so tame that one rubbed up against the side of the ship, as a friendly cat might do. It almost overturned the ship before the men's shouts frightened it away.

The *Hopewell* lay in Whale Bay for two or three days, waiting for a favorable wind. This time, it was the mate who asked permission to go ashore. Since the Captain refused to hear them, the mate had had to try to quiet the sailors' grumbling. They were especially tired of the food they had to eat.

Colman came to tell the Captain that he had seen a flock of wild geese flying toward the land. He thought if he could get a few with his musket it would make a welcome change from the everlasting salt meat.

Rather unwillingly the Captain gave permission. Colman and three other men rowed ashore. John would have liked to go too, but he was ashamed to ask. His father thought the shore trip silly. The boy was not going to admit that he wanted to do this silly thing.

It really *was* silly, as Colman and his companions

soon found out. They had not been ashore half an hour when a strong northeast gale sprang up, bringing with it a thick fog. The *Hopewell* was tossed about the shallow bay, and Captain Hudson was hard put to prevent the ship's being dashed against the rocky shore.

Those aboard the *Hopewell* had no way of guiding the rowboat to them except by sound. At the Captain's order, all the men began to bawl out their loudest songs. They sang until they were hoarse, going through "Spanish Ladies" and "How Many Wives Has a Sailor True," with its rollicking counting chorus, which leads up to "Fifty for me and fifty for you."

Night had fallen by the time the shore party groped its way to the ship. They were unharmed, "by God's mercie," as Hudson noted in his log. They had shot no geese, but they brought some deer horns, walrus teeth, and whalebones which they had picked up on the shore. They reported that they had seen footprints of bears and foxes, but not the animals themselves.

Hudson did not pretend to be interested in their finds. He had had enough of Whale Bay. If they were ever to get to China, they must press on.

They did press on, as soon as the weather allowed. They went far enough to convince the Captain that there was no way north. The only open water lay to the east, and it was thick with floating ice. More than once the *Hopewell* had barely escaped being crushed like an eggshell.

In late July, Captain Hudson gave up and turned homeward. He had done all that he could, but all he had done was in vain.

They followed much the same path by which they had come, except that they kept more to the east. This course brought them in sight of an unknown island, which they named "Hudson's Tutches." It is now called Jan Mayen Island. There were whales here, too.

Jan Mayen Island is the only original discovery Hudson made on this first voyage. And the abundance of whales there and at Spitsbergen was all that made the voyage of any importance.

To Captain Hudson, the expedition had been a total failure. There was not, as he had hoped, any way of reaching China by sailing over the North Pole. He must report to the Muscovy Company that they had wasted their money in backing him.

He reached London in early September. With a heavy heart, he sought out the directors to tell them his doleful news.

"I Am Not a Hunter!"

THE gentlemen of the Muscovy Company received Hudson in the warehouse room which served as office. It was a cozy room, comfortably furnished with a round table and armchairs. A coal fire snapped cheerfully in the grate, tempering the chill autumn air.

On his first visit, Captain Hudson had been offered a seat at the table. Today they kept him standing. The chairman addressed him sharply.

"Well, sir, what have you to say for yourself? We know already that the voyage was a failure. You persuaded us that you could reach China by the northern route. We invested good money in the undertaking, money which is now lost. We are not interested in excuses. It is a fact, is it not, that you failed to keep your promise?"

"No, sir, that is not a fact." Captain Hudson spoke with careful respect. "I would remind your worships that my promise was to seek a route to China by sailing north. I never promised that I would succeed. I hoped I would. I thought I would. But my promise was to make the attempt. That promise I kept. I did sail north, as far as I could go. That I could go no farther is a bitter disappointment to me."

"We are not interested in your disappointment," the chairman answered curtly. "Let us keep to the facts. You have satisfied yourself, then, that it is impossible to find a short route to China by way of the North?"

"Not at all," Hudson replied. There was eagerness in his voice, but he kept it low and steady. "I am more convinced than ever that it can be done. I was mistaken in thinking I could sail in a straight line over the Pole. But I am certain now that I could do it by turning east at Spitsbergen. I do earnestly believe that there is a northeastern passage to the Orient. I would like—"

"You would like to go looking for it," one of the directors cut in. "At our expense, of course." His disagreeable laugh was echoed around the table.

Hudson did not flinch. "Yes, gentlemen, that is what I was about to propose. I found open water to the east of Spitsbergen. We were hampered by floating ice, and we were running short of food. Also, the men were growing restive. It was a worthless crew I had, sirs; I can't conceal it. There was some damage from the ice, which my carpenter was quite unable to repair. For all these reasons, I was forced to turn back. But I firmly believe that if I could have continued in the easterly direction, I should have come to my goal."

"You chose your crew," one of the directors said coldly. "If they were worthless, you have only yourself to blame."

"Yes, sir," Hudson answered. "I blame myself for many mistakes on this voyage. I know now that we could depend on fishing and shooting for part of our food supply. I took too little in the way of fishing tackle and hunting weapons. Oh, I learned a great deal from this experience. Using what I learned, a second voyage—"

"Enough, Captain Hudson." The chairman's voice bore him down. "There will be no second voyage, so far as the Muscovy Company is concerned. You have a persuasive tongue, sir, but it will not fool us a second time."

He glanced around the table, to be met with nods of agreement.

For a minute Hudson studied the stony faces. Not one showed any ray of sympathy. These were businessmen. They had already lost a good deal of money, with nothing to show for it. It was hopeless to try to persuade them to risk more.

He sighed. "Very well. Then it remains only to submit my report."

He unrolled the parchment on which he had carefully noted every stage of the journey. In firm, steady tones he began to read it out.

There did not seem much in it to interest his hearers. He had mapped the east Greenland coast to a point farther north than any map showed. He had rediscovered the island of Spitsbergen, unvisited since the Dutchman Barents located it eleven years before. Hudson's map showed Spitsbergen's bays and mountains, with the names he had given them. His report mentioned the great number of whales in Spitsbergen waters.

It was the mention of the whales which suddenly roused the directors to attention. He was stopped in mid-sentence by the chairman.

"Whales, Captain Hudson? We had heard nothing of this. Whales live in Biscay Bay, and the confounded Spanish allow no one but themselves to hunt them. You say there are whales up there in the frozen North? Are you sure? Perhaps they were not whales at all, but merely great fish."

Hudson looked bewildered. "Oh, I assure you they were whales, sir. I have seen the Biscay whales myself, so I could not be mistaken. It is true that these creatures are larger than those of the South. And never have I seen them in such numbers. We could scarcely steer our way among them."

All around the table, the directors showed eager interest. England had no whaling industry, and no hope of any. The Spanish and the French, whose shores fringed the Bay of Biscay, kept it greedily in their own hands. Once in a while an English ship

made a whaling raid into Biscay waters. This involved a risk of war, which King James frowned upon.

And now, according to Hudson, there were whales in the northern waters, which belonged to no one. The directors' displeasure was forgotten as they plied the Captain with excited questions.

He answered as best he could, scarcely able to hide his surprise. He was a seafaring man, and nothing more. He had seen whales, as he had seen icebergs. He reported them both. One seemed no more important to him than the other.

To the directors, whales were extremely important.

Whale oil is nasty stuff, with a horrid smell. It is amusing to know that it was reserved for the nobility, along with fine wines and perfumes. An excellent soap could be made of it, and soap was strictly an upper-class luxury. The poor washed their coarse linen garments in plain water, scouring out the spots with sand. But the fashionable ruffs and laces of the court must be snowy white. Nothing, not even expensive olive-oil soap, did the job so well as soap made from whale blubber.

There was another court use for whale products.

Queen Elizabeth had introduced the fashion of the tiny waist. She was dead now, and King James ruled in her stead. But the fashion persisted. Court ladies laced themselves into rigid corsets to make their waists small. And for stiffening these garments, there was nothing like whalebone.

These were some of the reasons why the directors saw a fortune in whale-hunting. Once there was enough for the demands of fashion, the oil would have other uses. It could be used to grease carriage wheels, and the guns of the Royal Navy. It could be burned in lamps. There was no limit to the possibilities. If only Englishmen could get a whale supply of their own!

Again and again, Captain Hudson answered the same questions. Yes, he was sure the creatures in the Spitsbergen waters were whales. Never having been hunted, they were as tame as house cats. And yes, there were lots and lots of them, more than the eye could count.

The directors' friendliness grew as he gave satisfactory answers. Soon he was seated at the table, his map spread out before him. On it he traced the route to Spitsbergen.

He explained that there was no need to go, as

he had done, by way of Greenland. Straight north was the quickest route, through the North Sea and into the Norwegian Sea. Then a little way to the east, and there was Spitsbergen. Here on the map was the spot he had named Whale Bay. Yes, it made a pretty good harbor. His own ship had had one rough day there, but that was an exceptional storm. In ordinary weather, the bay was sheltered enough. The greatest danger came from the whales, which were so thick that a ship had to steer a careful passage among them.

This bit of news made the directors' eyes glisten. So many whales meant so much wealth, theirs for the taking. They lost no time in planning a Spitsbergen expedition.

It was taken for granted that Hudson would lead it. The failure of his China mission was forgiven and forgotten. The directors were stunned when he politely refused to take part in the new venture.

"I will give it all the help in my power," he explained. "My maps are at your disposal. I'll be glad to tell your captain everything I know. But I am an explorer. I am not a whale-hunter."

In vain they argued with him.

"It will make you rich, man!" the chairman urged. "The profits will be enormous. And we'll see that a fair share comes your way. No one but a fool would refuse such an opportunity."

Captain Hudson smiled.

"Perhaps I am a fool, gentlemen. I am a poor man. I see quite well that this is my chance of making a fortune. But I have never envied the rich. I have other hopes, other dreams. A man must be true to his own nature, or he is no man at all. I beg you, sirs, not to press me further. I will do everything I can to aid the Spitsbergen enterprise. But I will not sail with it."

They gave up at last. The first whaling ship sailed without him. Spitsbergen was claimed for England, and an industry began. It was later disputed by the Dutch, who set up their own outpost there. What happened then is a story in itself, a fascinating one that runs down into the nineteenth century. It is no part of the story of Henry Hudson.

Captain Hudson kept his promise and acted as adviser to the Company's whaling undertaking.

But always, quietly and persistently, he kept pleading his own cause. He wanted to search for a northeastern passage to China.

Perhaps out of gratitude, perhaps to silence him, the directors finally surrendered. Since he was so set upon it, they would back him in a new expedition.

Two Men

ON a windy day in late March, Hudson went down to the docks to inspect his ship. It was the *Hopewell*, the same one he had used on the first voyage. He had ordered some changes. Stouter masts were being fitted. The hull was being reinforced with extra planks, to resist the grinding ice floes. There was also a stronger and larger ship's boat.

The work was almost finished. Only one carpenter was still busy, replacing a broken plank. He looked up and touched his cap respectfully as the Captain approached.

"You would be the master, sir? I hope you find everything to your satisfaction."

"It looks very well," Hudson answered.

He lingered a minute, watching the man's skillful hands.

The carpenter was a big, rawboned fellow, with a shock of yellow hair and a red, honest face. Every hammer stroke rang straight and true, driving the nails through the thick board as though it were cheese.

"I see you know your trade, fellow," Hudson remarked.

The man laughed. "I ought to, Master. Worked in the shipbuilding yards, I did, before I went to sea."

"You're a sailor as well, then?"

"Able-bodied seaman, sir. *And* ship's carpenter. Name of Philip Staffe. Ready to turn to when there's a carpenter job at sea. But that don't mean I shirk my turn at the ropes. A hard worker I am, sir, whatever I'm set to do. If so be you're signing

on hands for this voyage, sir, I'd like fine to sail with you."

"You would?" Hudson did not hesitate. "Then you can consider yourself hired, Staffe. Our ship took a lot of damage from the ice up north. It needs a good man to make repairs on the spot, and my last ship's carpenter was— Well, never mind. Bring your papers when you come to work tomorrow. If I find them in order, the job is yours."

"They'll be all shipshape," Staffe answered. His face broke into a broad grin. "And thankee, sir. I'll do my best to give satisfaction."

Hudson nodded, and turned away. This, he felt, was a good beginning. He was giving serious thought to the selection of his men this time. Of his old ship's company, he wanted to rehire only two. He would have been glad to have Colman, the mate, but Colman had already signed on for the Company's whaling expedition. The two men he chose, Cooke and Skrutton, were not too unsatisfactory. He hoped he could get a really good crew together for this second voyage.

He finished looking over the ship and made his way home. John came to meet him with a bit of news.

"There was a man here to see you, Father. He wants to go with us as mate. He's been all over the world—to Turkey, and to Africa, and even to New Spain! He's been in storms, and shipwrecks, and he's fought pirates, too. He's not afraid of anything. We'll take him, won't we, Father? He's just the man we need."

Hudson smiled and turned to his wife. "And what did you think of this hero, my dear?"

"Talks too much," Mrs. Hudson said briefly. "And he's got a shifty eye. I wouldn't have him in the house."

Captain Hudson laughed. "A man you wouldn't have in the house might be a very useful man aboard ship, love. Well, we'll see. Is he coming back?"

"He said you could find him at the White Swan after supper," John Hudson put in. "I promised you'd go and talk to him. You'll like him, I know you will. He's got a full-rigged man-o'-war tattooed on his arm, and—"

"Enough," Hudson interrupted. "I see supper's on the table. I'll go along to the White Swan later."

John would have liked to go, too, but his father did not ask him. Captain Hudson finished his meal and made his way to the near-by tavern. It was customary to transact small business in the ale-houses, where men could meet and talk quietly over a mug of beer.

He found the stranger already seated on a high-backed settle in a corner.

Robert Juet was older than Hudson had expected—well on in the fifties, at a guess. But he jumped to his feet nimbly enough, welcoming the Captain with a deep bow.

"Will you please to be seated, sir? I'll just fetch you a tankard of ale. Mild, will it be, or bitter? Half-and-half? Right, sir. There's nothing like a pint of half-and-half to take off the evening's chill, I always say. Half a minute, sir."

Hudson frowned as he took his seat. Katherine was right. The man did talk too much.

Returning, the sailor caught the frown. Instantly his manner changed.

"You'll be wanting to know more about me, Master," he said humbly. "A smart captain like you don't take a mate on his own say-so, that I know. Here are my seaman's papers. And some letters from captains I've served under."

Hudson glanced over the papers. They were all

in order. The captains' letters mentioned that Juet had unusual skill at navigation, and was "clean, sober and respectful."

Laying them aside, Captain Hudson asked some questions of his own. Juet answered them readily and modestly. He had indeed traveled widely, as he had told John. But he did not repeat the adventurous tales which had so impressed the boy.

"You seem to know navigation as well as many captains," Hudson remarked approvingly. "You say you've never commanded a ship yourself, Juet? I should think you might have tried for such a post."

The man's eyes flashed. "I've tried, many's the time, sir. But they won't have me." Then he went on more calmly. "I learned my sailoring the hard way, serving before the mast. And owners want an educated man, like you are. It's just my luck that I never had a chance to go to school. But if I could just get a command, just once, I'd show 'em as good a captain as ever sailed the seas. Oh, well—" He broke off. "You won't be caring about my troubles, Master. All I can say is, if you take me on I'll serve you well."

Hudson asked a few more questions. The man's

knowledge of navigation was certainly beyond that commonly expected of a mate. If he seemed a little overpolite, a little too fawning and anxious to please—well, those were small faults. Before the evening ended, Juet was accepted for the post he desired.

So, in one day, Captain Hudson began his association with two men, the carpenter Philip Staffe and the mate Robert Juet. He thought merely that he was signing on two competent men for a single voyage. He could not know that these men would each play a leading part in his life, and in his death.

Novaya Zemlya

THE new mate began at once to prove himself a treasure. He took over all the tiresome details of preparation. Armed with a list of stores required, he attended to the purchases and their delivery. Captain Hudson, always impatient of such matters, gladly turned the business over to him.

Juet made himself equally useful in recruiting the crew. Only three men had been hired so far; Cooke and Skrutton from the first voyage, and the carpenter, Staffe. Juet, with far less trouble than Hudson had had, quickly filled out the company to fourteen. Two of the men he chose, Michael Perse and Arnold Lodlo, may have been old shipmates of his, although this is not certain. At any rate, they were completely devoted to him, ready to follow his lead in all things.

All was ready by mid-April. At the last minute, Captain Hudson had a bit of luck. He fell in with a Norwegian sea captain employed by the Muscovy Company. This man had just returned from a voyage to the Russian port of Archangel, where the Company had a trading post. He was able to give Hudson a corrected map of the Norwegian coast and valuable information on winds and weather in the Barents Sea.

The Barents Sea was the body of water which separated Spitsbergen and the Russian island of Novaya Zemlya. It was through its waters that Hudson hoped to sail on his new quest. And it was in these waters that the ice had turned him back the first time, before ever he came in sight of Novaya Zemlya.

This time, he meant to keep considerably south of his old route. There would still be ice, but it seemed reasonable to expect that it would be less solid there. The ship, with new and stronger planks, would be in less danger from the floating ice. Captain Hudson was confident that he could thread his way through.

The *Hopewell* sailed on April 22, 1608. Skirting the west Norwegian coast, they headed north until they rounded the Scandinavian peninsula. Here they turned east. There was floating ice about, but plenty of clear green water between the cakes.

For nearly a week the gallant little vessel nosed her way along, making slow but steady progress. Then the ice closed in.

It was the story of the first voyage over again. The great floes shifted and moved, narrowing the channels between them. It took all of Hudson's superb seamanship to keep the *Hopewell* twisting and dodging to the northern tip of the Russian island. It was here that he had expected to pass through into the Kara Sea beyond. To his bitter disappointment, the ice offered no clear passage.

Captain Hudson headed south, along the western coast of Novaya Zemlya. This is a long, thin island, like a pickle standing on end. The Russians owned it, but had never settled it. Only their hunters came to the island from time to time, seeking wild fowl and walruses.

Novaya Zemlya's coast has many inlets and bays. Hudson hoped that one of these might be a strait, leading all the way across the island and into the Kara Sea. For several weeks he ranged up and down the coast, seeking for a strait which is not there.

It was an infuriating time for Hudson, whose only aim was to get on with his exploring. For everyone else aboard, it was quite pleasant.

Novaya Zemlya in the summertime bubbled with little streams of melting snow. The sun shone brightly. Short-lived Arctic grass was springing up out of the mud. Seabirds were nesting on the rocky shore.

One day, the mate, Juet, came to the Captain.

"If I say it as shouldn't, sir," he began modestly, "I'm a fair hand with a gun. Some of these sea fowl make good eating, if they're young enough. And there must be eggs to be found. If so be you'd let a few of us go ashore, we could bring back a change of food. The men would appreciate that, sir."

Hudson had heard this before, on his first voyage. "Are the men grumbling about the food?"

he asked sharply. "They've made no complaint to me."

Juet looked shocked. "I should hope not, sir! I've got them under better discipline than that. 'The Captain's not to be bothered,' I tell them. 'He's got important things on his mind. Any complaints you got, you bring 'em to me and I'll see to it. That's what the mate is for.' I don't think they've given you any trouble so far, sir."

"No, they haven't," Hudson admitted. "Very civil and willing I've found them. Quite different from the last lot I had. I admire the way you handle them, Juet. And I appreciate being relieved of bothering with them."

"I'm only doing my duty, sir. As I see it, it's the mate's job to take these little things off the captain's hands. It makes me happy to hear you say that I'm satisfying you, sir. Now this business of food —it means a lot to them, to have a little change in their eating. And today is a good time. The wind's dead calm. We're stuck here offshore in any case. I can't see that a small shore party could do any harm. But of course it's for you to say, Master."

Hudson thought for a minute. Juet was quite

right in saying that they would not be moving on until a favoring wind sprang up.

The Captain himself had no interest in a change of diet. Ship's food was ship's food; he ate what was provided without giving it a thought. Nor had he any curiosity about this land which lay so near. Novaya Zemlya was Russian territory which could not be claimed for England. So far as Hudson was concerned, the island was simply an obstacle in his path.

Juet saw his hesitation and pressed on.

"I won't deny that the men are getting a little restless, some of them. A chance to stretch their legs ashore would do them a world of good. And it would only be for a few hours. We'd keep in sight of the ship, and hurry back if you signaled us. Of course I'd only take a few with me. Maybe three or four. With respect, sir, I think it would be a good thing if you could see your way clear to giving permission."

"Oh, very well," Hudson said impatiently. "Mind, though, you're not to go out of sight. The breeze may spring up at any minute. Which men had you thought of taking?"

"Lodlo and Perse," the mate answered promptly.

"They claim to be fine shots. And a couple of others."

Young John Hudson had been sitting quietly by. Now he looked imploringly at his father. It had been made plain to the boy that he was to expect no favors because he was the Captain's son. Just the same, he ventured to speak now.

"I'm a good climber, Father. If I went, I know I could reach the highest rocks where the nests are."

Robert Juet spoke before the Captain could answer.

"Oh, no, Master John. That would never do. What if you fell and broke a leg on them rocks? The Captain would blame me. I wouldn't want the responsibility of taking him, sir."

Captain Hudson was already turning back to his charts.

"That's all right," he said absently. "John doesn't need to go. If you can't find anything else to do, son, you can get on with your scrimshaw work. That will be all, Juet. Pick what men you choose, but remember, don't wander too far or stay too long."

"Yes, sir. Thank you, sir. You'll have a nice dish

of fowl for your supper, Master, and fried eggs for tomorrow's breakfast."

The mate hurried off. From the cabin porthole, John watched the launching of the boat. Then, sighing, he settled again to his carving.

On a walrus tusk he was scratching out a design of ship and waves, with stars overhead. This scrimshaw work, done with a pocketknife and shoemaker's awl, was a favorite occupation of sailors on long voyages. John was very good at it. The decorated tusk, strung on ribbons, would be an ornament for his mother's parlor wall.

Man and boy worked on in silence until Captain Hudson got up to find a new pen. Then John spoke.

"It's funny, Father. Mr. Juet doesn't seem to like me at all. He was so nice to me that day he came to our house. I thought we were going to be friends. But since the voyage started, he's had no use for me. He's always with the men in the forecastle, talking, and telling jokes, and playing dice with them. If I go in there, they tell me to run away. Do you think I've offended Mr. Juet? I didn't mean to."

Captain Hudson smiled. "You're imagining things, son. Naturally, grown men don't have much time for young boys. And sailors' talk is pretty rough. I'd just as soon you didn't get too thick with any of the crew. Juet handles them his own way, and he's doing splendidly. Let him alone. You and I have each other for company. And I must say you're more company to me than any shipmate I've ever had. I can talk to you about what I'm trying to do as I couldn't to anyone else. You're a bright boy, John. Having you along is a real comfort to me."

The boy's thin face flushed with pleasure. It was not often that his father spoke such words of praise. He had tried very hard to earn it. He was learning navigation, quickly and easily, under his father's direction. One day he too would be a captain. His dearest wish was to be just such a captain as his father; to go exploring to far places and make discoveries no one else had made. He felt ashamed now that he had wanted to waste time on such childish occupations as hunting birds' eggs.

He was too shy to express all that he felt. Instead he could only say simply: "I'd rather be here with you, anyway. There's nothing to see on that old island. And you'll want to go ashore yourself when we come to China, won't you, Father?"

"Indeed I will, and you shall go too. All those golden cities with their palaces—we'll explore them together, you and I. That's a promise."

It was a promise with which John was happily content. All through the quiet afternoon he sat at his father's side, working away at his carving. Occasionally they could hear bursts of gunfire from the shore. It was nearly suppertime when the landing party returned.

In spite of his boasts, Juet and his friends had not done too well with their shooting. They brought one seagull, so old and tough that it could only be used for soup. However, they had filled their caps with eggs, which made a welcome addition to the evening meal. They had also picked up some deer horns and whalebones, and a piece of a wooden cross erected by the Russians long ago.

The next day, the *Hopewell* resumed her cruising up and down the island coast, probing for an opening. Several appeared promising, but always dwindled into blind alleys when followed up. A few more landings were made, but again the hunting was poor. Although walruses were plentiful, the sailors had no luck at killing any.

So far as is known, neither Captain Hudson nor his son ever set foot on the Russian island. Even Juet, who had hoped for some sort of treasure, lost interest when none was found. The one thing Captain Hudson hoped to find, a way to the sea beyond, did not exist. After several weeks of useless searching, he was obliged to give up.

They turned homeward, reaching London on August 27, a little more than four months from the day they set sail.

Again Captain Hudson had failed to find a passage to the East. This second voyage was even more disappointing than the first. That one had at least opened up the whaling industry to England. The second voyage had accomplished nothing whatever, except to prove that one could not reach China by the northeastern route.

The Muscovy Company had not risked its good money for such a poor result. Many of the directors were already convinced that the route did not exist. They did not consider it worth the cost of the voyage to prove it. Captain Hudson's interview to report results was not a pleasant one. He was told, flatly and angrily, that he might now consider his employment by the Company at an end.

To Amsterdam

THE failure of his two voyages for the Muscovy Company was a bitter disappointment to Captain Hudson. But whatever he felt, he did not for one minute give up his dream of finding a short route to the Orient. There were other companies; other wealthy merchants who might be willing to back a third voyage.

Patiently he made the rounds. Sometimes he was

politely refused. Sometimes he did not even obtain an interview. One October afternoon he waited from noon to dusk to see a director who finally sent out word that he had no time for him.

Captain Hudson had missed his supper while he sat in the outer office. Leaving the warehouse, he stopped in at a waterside tavern.

He carried bread and cheese and ale to a table by the window. He had scarcely settled himself when he saw a familiar figure enter the door.

Hudson stood up and beckoned. "Captain Smith!" he called. "Will you join me?"

The tall man with the battle-scarred face turned, and then limped over to him. The two shook hands warmly. At Hudson's order, the waiter brought a tankard of ale for the newcomer.

"You are back from Virginia, then?" Hudson asked. "I had not heard. I knew that the Jamestown colony was going well. I had supposed you would stay there as governor."

Captain John Smith smiled bitterly.

"His Majesty the King has relieved me," he answered. "He was glad enough of my services in founding the colony. Now that it is prospering, he has appointed another gentleman to govern it. Oh,

I do not complain. I have another project closer to my heart."

"Yes? And what may that be?"

"I am waiting now for permission to explore the American coast north of Virginia. There is a vast land there, of which we know very little. I hope to be given a ship to map the New England coast-line all the way north."

"Then indeed you have no complaint," Hudson observed. "As I remember you, you'd rather explore than settle down. And I feel the same way. I have always had more interest in the sea than in the land."

"I know," Smith answered. "It has been—how long?—nearly three years since you wished me Godspeed when I sailed for Virginia. You were hoping then to seek a way to China over the North Pole. Did you go? Did you find it? I have had no news of you since our last meeting. Tell me how things have gone with you."

"They have not gone well," Hudson answered soberly. Then, under sympathetic questioning, he poured out the whole story of his two unsuccessful voyages.

"And now you see me, an unemployed captain,"

he ended. "Oh, I could get a ship easily enough, in ordinary trade. But my heart is not in it. I still have hopes of reaching the Orient, by one direction if not by another. Lately, I have been wondering if a northwest passage would not be possible."

"Why not?" Smith said. "The Cabots, when they discovered Newfoundland, reported many gulfs and streams. Any one of them might lead through the continent to the Pacific."

"Yes, and there was Captain Davis's 'Furious Overfall,'" Hudson said eagerly. "Do you remember how he described it? 'We saw the sea falling down into a gulf with a mighty overfall, as streams pass through the arches of bridges.' Davis saw only the mouth of that gulf. Neither he nor John Cabot tried to penetrate inland. They contented themselves with following the coastline. If one could get a ship past the Overfall and sail up the gulf— Well, who knows?"

"I'm not so sure about the Furious Overfall," Smith said. "It's pretty far north. If you remember, Davis spoke of ice floes carried on the swift current of the gulf. Fighting that current, with the ice bearing down on you, would be dangerous and difficult. You've had more experience with ice than

I have. But I confess it would discourage me."

"I've had as much experience with ice as I want," Hudson said frankly. "I'd be delighted if I could find a passage farther to the south. But I have no reason to think that one exists."

"No? Well, then, this may interest you. Our Indians in Virginia tell stories of an ocean lying to the west. It can only be the Pacific. How far it is, or how it may be reached, they cannot say. One old man told me that his ancestors lived on the ocean shore, and came to Virginia by canoe. He may be lying, of course. But if there is truth in his story, there must be a waterway between the two oceans."

Hudson leaned forward, keenly interested. "And is there such a waterway in Virginia?"

"In Virginia, no. But the coastline north of Virginia is largely unknown. It is this region that I hope to map, when the King gives his permission. But we know that there are many gulfs and inlets. They may be the mouths of rivers. Or one of them may be a strait, leading to the western ocean. It might be worth your while to find out. At least, you would be free of the troublesome ice."

"You've given me something to think about,"

Hudson said. "Tell me all that you remember of the Indians' stories."

Captain Smith did the best he could, repeating the tales as he had heard them. We know now that the "ocean" of which the natives spoke was probably Lake Erie. If the ancestors of the Virginia Indians had come from there by canoe, they must have done it by way of rivers and smaller streams, impassable to oceangoing ships. But it all sounded very convincing to Captain Hudson.

"It's worth trying," he said. "One thing is sure. I have given up all hope of a northeastern passage. If there is a way, it must lie northwest, through the Furious Overfall, or farther south. A man could explore both in a single voyage, couldn't he?"

"Yes, and you're the man to do it," Smith said heartily. "And I hope you will."

Hudson sighed. "How can I? I'd need a ship, and ships cost money, Captain Smith. I've been trying desperately to interest men who could supply it. But, so far, they have all refused me."

"Well, don't be discouraged. Your problem is easier than mine. I am under royal orders. The Virginia Company would give me a ship, but I cannot move until our lord the King appoints me his official mapmaker. And his Majesty has very little interest in exploration. Sometimes I wish I had never taken service with the Crown. But you are a private person. All you have to do is to find other private persons who will furnish the money."

"All I have to do," Hudson echoed sadly. "And that is the one thing I cannot do."

"Oh, you'll manage it," Smith answered. "I know a few wealthy merchants who might listen to me. I'll speak to them about you."

Hudson thanked him and rose to go. It was late. His wife would be wondering what had become of him. They parted, agreeing to meet again soon. And by that time, Smith said cheerfully, he hoped to bring some good news.

They met several times, but the news was never good. Captain John Smith did his best. However, the rich merchants had heard of Hudson's two failures. None of them wanted to risk money on an explorer who had disappointed the powerful Muscovy Company.

Just when things were looking blackest, a gleam of hope came. Captain Hudson received a letter from a Dutch friend.

This was the scholar-geographer Peter Plancius,

one of the men who had argued that it must be warm at the North Pole. It was by quoting Plancius that Hudson had impressed the directors at his first interview. Plancius and Hudson had never met, but they had long known each other by correspondence.

Now the Hollander was writing to ask if Hudson would care to take service with the Dutch East India Company. This company already had a brisk trade with the Orient. But their ships had to sail all the way around Africa, a journey which sometimes took three years. If a shorter route could be found, the East India Company would be delighted. Plancius thought it would be well worth while for Hudson to come to Amsterdam and press his plan.

Henry Hudson asked nothing better. So long as he might get on with his exploring, he cared not at all whether he did it for England or for Holland. With all his hopes renewed, he hurried off to Amsterdam.

There he found an unexpected difficulty. Plancius was as certain as ever that the hoped-for route lay to the north. The old scholar had written a book to prove that the climate at the North Pole was temperate. He stubbornly maintained that Hudson had given up too soon on his first voyage. If he had proceeded straight north, penetrating the fringe of ice, he would have found warm water leading easily to China.

"Perhaps your ship was at fault," he said kindly. "The English do not know how to build ships which can penetrate the ice. In a good stout Dutch ship, you would have no trouble."

Captain Hudson sighed. He had sailed those ice-laden waters, while Plancius sat snugly in his library, working it all out on paper. The old man had staked his scientific reputation on his calculations. He would not listen to any suggestion that they might be wrong.

All Hudson's arguments were in vain. In vain, too, he brought up the matter of a northwest or southwest passage. Dr. Plancius was not interested. If Captain Hudson wished to attempt the North again, the good doctor would use his influence with the Company to back the undertaking. Otherwise, there was no chance.

The discussions dragged on for weeks. It was a trying time for Captain Hudson. He wanted, above all else, to be given a ship. Plancius was sure the Company would give him one, if he sailed to the north.

In the end, Plancius offered a compromise. He agreed that the expedition might turn east on reaching the opening between Spitsbergen and Novaya Zemlya. Further than that he would not go.

This meant the old Northeast Passage again; the one Hudson had sought in vain on his second voyage. It was true that he had not spent too much time looking for a way between the two islands. He had turned south, seeking a strait through Novaya Zemlya. Plancius was sure this had been a mistake. If he had kept on probing north of the Russian island, he would have found a way. In a good Dutch ship, he was sure to find it.

Hudson agreed at last, because he had no choice. If he continued to refuse, the Dutch would have none of him. And he *had* to go exploring! He told himself that perhaps Plancius was right. Maybe he had given up too soon. Maybe the Dutch ship would make the difference. Finally he agreed, and promised to sail as the Company directed.

Once this was settled, Plancius introduced him to the directors. They took a maddening time to consider it, even though the old scholar pressed his case for him.

While the Company hesitated, Hudson received a half-offer from the French. There was nothing certain about it, but the French representative in Amsterdam hinted that France might be interested in a search for the Northeast Passage.

Word of this came to the Dutch company. The last thing they wanted was for their rivals, the French, to find a short cut to the Orient. Delaying no longer, they summoned Hudson and offered him a contract.

The contract was not a flattering one. The Dutch did not completely trust an Englishman. They insisted that half his crew be Dutch, with a Dutch mate. They laid out his exact course on the map, turning east above Novaya Zemlya. In plain words the contract stated that he was "to think of discovering no other routes or passages, except the route around by the north and northeast of Novaya Zemlya."

The Company undertook to provide a ship, the *Half Moon*, to provision it, and to pay the crew. The Captain's own pay was on the stingy side. He was to receive what would be about $208 in our money. If he did not return alive, his widow would be paid the princely sum of $52. He was to have no share in any profits from the expedition, all such going to the Company.

A copy of this contract still exists. It is written in Dutch, with an English translation on the back. The Captain's signature is a plain "Henry Hudson." There is no excuse for calling him, as some histories do, "Hendrik." He knew no Dutch, and never thought of giving up his English citizenship. He was an Englishman working for a Dutch company. He dressed as an Englishman. The picture of Dutch *Hendrik* and his men given in Irving's "Rip Van Winkle" is pure fancy. This third voyage was the only one Captain Hudson ever made for the Dutch, and the only connection he ever had with them.

Westward Ho!

WHEN news of the new expedition reached England, Captain Hudson had a letter from John Colman, the mate of his first voyage. He was at liberty, and anxious to sail again with his old captain. If a mate had already been chosen, he wrote, he would be willing to sign on as a common seaman.

Hudson had planned to take the useful Robert Juet as first mate, but was not to be allowed to do so. The Dutch company insisted on putting in their own man for that post. The best the Captain had been allowed to offer Juet was a place as second mate. Somewhat to his surprise, Juet had agreed willingly enough.

Their reasons for accepting the reduction in rank were as different as the two men themselves. Honest John Colman made his offer out of devotion to Captain Hudson.

There was no room for devotion in Juet's black, jealous heart. Spiteful, malicious, a born trouble-maker, he had nothing but contempt for his easy going superior. Just the same, it suited him very well to serve under Captain Hudson. With him, he was allowed more authority than he had ever known. On the Novaya Zemlya voyage, Juet had come close to taking the Captain's place in all but the most important matters. Hudson had been relieved to turn over the supervision of the crew to his efficient mate. Such a chance would not come again with another captain. Mr. Juet did not mean to lose it.

Humbly accepting second place, he offered to recruit the English crew and bring them along to

Amsterdam. Once again Hudson was glad to have this detail taken off his hands.

Juet chose his best friends from among the old crew. He was not happy at having to accept Colman, but he managed to leave out Philip Staffe, the carpenter. He could have done without John Hudson, too, but here he had no choice. Except for Colman and John, he was sure of support from all the Englishmen. As soon as he reached Amsterdam, he began to cultivate the Dutch section.

Juet either knew, or learned quickly, something of the Dutch language. The Dutch mate, a stupid, well-meaning fellow, thought him a splendid new friend. Even before they sailed, Juet had the Dutchman on his side.

The *Half Moon* sailed from Amsterdam on March 25, 1609. The weather was bad from the beginning. It took the ship more than a month to beat her way to the northern tip of Norway. This is the point at which they were supposed to turn eastward toward Novaya Zemlya. And it is the point at which Captain Hudson encountered his first outright mutiny. There is good reason to believe that Juet promoted it. It is certain at least that he encouraged it, out of sheer malice.

He came to the cabin with the news. Bowing and scraping, as he always did for the Captain, he began his story.

"It's sorry I am to tell you this, sir. But I think you should know. The Dutch sailors are making trouble. All of them are lying in their bunks this morning, refusing to get up."

"Why?" the Captain asked. "Are they sick?"

"No, sir. They're cold. And they won't leave their warm beds. Of course, it's the Dutch mate's job to order them up, but he won't do it. Fact is, Master, he's lying in *his* bunk, with his blankets pulled over his head. I had to stand his watch last night. Not that I mind the extra work," Juet went on virtuously, "but it's hard on our Englishmen. If this goes on, our men will have to work the ship alone. I thought you ought to know, sir."

"Certainly I ought," Hudson agreed. "But I don't understand this. They complain of the cold, you say? But they signed on for a voyage to the North. They must have known it would be cold."

"You'd think so, sir. But they say they didn't know what it would be like. And that's true enough. They've been employed in the East Indies trade, down in the Torrid Zone. I expect they complained about the heat there, for they're a complaining lot, sir. But the change from the tropics to the Arctic is too much for them, or so they say."

"Well, they'll have to get used to it," Hudson said briskly. He rose. "I'll go talk to them. You come along, Juet. You speak their language. I'll need you to translate for me."

The two men made their way to the forecastle, where the sailors slept. At the Captain's curt order, the men staggered sheepishly to their feet. Ignoring the others, Hudson spoke sharply to the Dutch mate. He would not tolerate any shirking, he told him. The Dutchmen were to turn to and relieve their English comrades at once.

Sullenly, they obeyed. Hudson went back to his cabin, convinced that the trouble was all over. He soon found that it was only beginning.

The next day, it was the English sailors who complained of the cold. All the men had good reason for such a complaint. The weather could scarcely have been worse. Heavy sleet storms coated the decks with ice. The sails and ropes froze to the stiffness of wood, making them almost impossible to handle. On top of this came wind and fog, and the increasing danger of running blindly into the floating ice. There were some bad falls on the icy deck, with broken arms and sprained shoulders and ankles. Several of the men were suffering from frostbite.

Every day, Robert Juet came to the Captain with some new story of the men's dissatisfaction. Secretly, he was encouraging the men in their rebellion. He was the sailors' friend. If *he* had been their captain, as by rights he ought to be, everything would have been different.

Captain Hudson knew nothing of this. He always kept apart from the men, preferring to let Juet handle them. It is sad but true that the Captain was completely taken in by this mischief-maker. The man had a smooth tongue and plausible manners. To the Captain he was humble and respectful, eager to carry out his master's orders. And all the while he was feeding the men's discontent, sympathizing with their troubles, indignant against a captain who could lead them into such disaster.

There was one man among the English crew who could have exposed the villainous Juet to Hudson. This was John Colman, who had sailed

with the first expedition. Colman was a simple, hardworking sailor to whom his captain's word was law. Unfortunately, his respect for authority extended to all the ship's officers. Juet, after all, was second mate. It was not for an ordinary seaman to criticize one superior to another. Colman held his tongue, and Hudson's blind faith in Juet was not disturbed.

For two weeks, the bad weather grew steadily worse. And, in those two weeks, the mutiny came to a head. Juet waited on the Captain one day with a new report. The men had flatly refused to continue the voyage. They demanded that the ship be turned about and headed for home.

"I've done my best to reason with them, sir," Juet declared. "But they're out of hand. They say they won't lift a finger until you agree. And I'm afraid they mean it, sir."

"Very well, Juet," Hudson answered quietly. "Tell them I will think it over. And muster them all on deck this evening. I'll give them my answer then. You may go now."

"Yes, sir." Juet took himself off, to report gleefully that the Captain would give in.

Hudson shut himself alone in the cabin for the

afternoon. We have no way of knowing what he thought. The law of the sea gave the captain full authority to suppress mutiny, even by the death penalty. In a similar situation, Sir Francis Drake had once with his own hand cut off the head of a mutinous mate. Queen Elizabeth commended this action as showing "admirable firmness."

There were few sea captains of that time who had not found use for the barbarous punishments permitted them. Henry Hudson had never employed them. His gentle, kindly nature forbade it. He could not do it now.

At the same time, he simply could not bring himself to give up the expedition and return to Amsterdam. He already had two unsuccessful voyages against him. A third one would finish his career as an explorer. There must be another way. And, thinking it all over in the solitude of his cabin, he found one.

It was a way which would not please the Dutch East India Company. Indeed, it meant openly disobeying the strict orders they had given him. It must have been difficult for him to bring himself to consider it. But try as he would, he could find no other.

Once he had decided upon it, his spirits rose. The rebellion was forcing him to do what he had wanted to do all along. If he succeeded in reaching China, he did not think the Company would reproach him for not doing it as they had expected. With a lightened heart, he faced the group of sullen men gathered on the deck that evening.

He began with a stern rebuke for the mutiny. He reminded them of the punishments he could impose if he chose. Furthermore, he pointed out that there was another thing he could do. If they forced him to return to Amsterdam, he could lodge a charge against them with his employers. Mutiny on the high seas was a serious crime. The directors could put them on trial in the courts. If found guilty, they would be certain of imprisonment, if not of death.

The men shuffled uneasily at this, and began to mutter among themselves. Juet had assured them that Captain Hudson was too soft-hearted to take extreme measures at sea. There was nothing soft-hearted about the gentlemen of the East India Company, who had expected results from this voyage.

Hudson gave them a few minutes to think it

over. Then, in a milder tone, he offered them a choice. As all of them could testify, the weather and the ice were making the northeastern course difficult, if not impossible. How would it be if, instead of going home, they turned to the west instead?

Carefully he explained the possibilities in that direction. They could head for the Furious Over-fall, on the North American coast. While still in the North, the Overfall lay ten degrees south of where they now were. The climate should be that much warmer.

He waited, but there was no response. Ten degrees warmer was not warm enough to please these bone-chilled sailors.

Then, Captain Hudson went on, there was still another way. Captain John Smith had assured him that a passage might be found in the temperate climate just north of Virginia. This was south of both England and Holland. The summer weather there would be at least as pleasant as they had been accustomed to at home.

This suggestion appealed to all of them. It appealed especially to Robert Juet, their leader. Instead of going home in disgrace, they might redeem themselves by finding China in comfort. And there was all that Oriental wealth if they succeeded. Mr. Juet, who liked to make trouble, liked even more to make money. Any profits were supposed to go to the Company. But a small bag of pearls, concealed under a sailor's shirt, could surely be smuggled ashore.

Juet spoke up for the new plan, and all the sailors joined him. Everyone was pleased, Captain Hudson not least of all. The meeting broke up with a hearty cheer for the Captain. The crew, who had protested they could not work in the cold, found that they could work perfectly well when it came to turning their ship for the new course.

The American Shore

AT their last meeting, Captain John Smith had given Hudson copies of his American maps. Hudson had taken them along to Amsterdam, where he used them to try to win Dutch approval for a western voyage. Dr. Plancius and other Dutch scholars had examined them with interest. But they refused to believe that there was a possible route in that direction. Regretfully, Hudson had put them away and brought out the old maps of Spitsbergen and Novaya Zemlya.

It was with great pleasure that he turned to the American maps now. Unlike Columbus, he was not sailing out into the unknown. Both North and South America appeared on the maps. Thanks to the Spanish, South America had been more thoroughly explored. But something had been learned of North America, even in the Far North. French and English explorers had discovered Labrador and Newfoundland. Some of them, including the Cabots, had followed the coastline as far south as the Carolinas. All of them had made maps. These maps were among those Smith lent to Captain Hudson with his own.

In the Cabots' day, North America had been completely new territory to Europeans. But now, more than a hundred years after the first Cabot voyage, the Atlantic coast had three settlements. The French, under Champlain, had claimed Canada, and founded the city of Quebec. The English were in Virginia. And to the south, the Spanish were occupying Florida.

It was only the middle stretch, between Canada and Virginia, that had not been thoroughly explored. This was the territory in which Hudson hoped to find his western passage. Accordingly, he laid out his course to touch land below Canada.

He did not quite make it. Actually, their first sight of land was the coast of Newfoundland. But by turning sharply south, he avoided French territory. A week later, on July 17, he came to anchor in Penobscot Bay, Maine.

The shore was fringed with huge pine trees, growing right down to the water's edge. This was a welcome sight, for a recent storm had carried away the *Half Moon's* foremast. A boat was making ready to go ashore when the newcomers had their first contact with the natives.

A canoe came out from the shore, carrying six Indians. They were friendly, and were delighted when the whites gave them food and some glass buttons. The next day, a larger party visited the ship, offering beaver skins in trade for the sailors' red jackets.

The *Half Moon* spent five or six days in Penobscot Bay. Minor repairs were made to the ship, and a new mast fitted. The sailors went fishing, catching vast quantities of halibut and cod. They also caught lobsters, which the Indians taught them to cook and shell. This new food was so delicious that at one shore dinner the men gorged themselves and were all sick the next day.

True to his custom, the Captain spent little time ashore. He was busy plotting their future course. Penobscot Bay was a pleasant place, but it led no-where. Once the ship was ready, the Captain was anxious to be off.

From Maine they sailed on southward, reaching Cape Cod near the point where the *Mayflower* was to touch land only eleven years later. Like the Pilgrims who came after them, the *Half Moon's* crew went ashore and brought back a fine haul of ripe wild grapes.

Continuing southward, they came to Virginia, almost within sight of the colony at Jamestown.

It might have been expected that they would pay a visit there. But Hudson had a good reason for not doing so. He was sailing under the Dutch flag. Smith was not at Jamestown. The colony was under an English governor whom Hudson did not know. It might well be that the Jamestown Eng-lish would not welcome a Dutch ship in their waters.

At any rate, Hudson had no interest in Virginia.

Captain Smith had assured him that there was no westward passage there. So, on August 19, the *Half Moon* turned and headed north again.

On their trip southward, the winds had kept them at sea, out of sight of land. They sailed closer to the coast on the way back. They entered Delaware Bay, pausing only long enough to make sure that it did not lead inland. Then they continued northward, keeping the land in sight.

Early on the morning of September 2, they rounded Sandy Hook to pass into Lower New York Bay. Of course none of these places had those names then. But it is easier to follow Hudson's progress by using the names we know today.

With a fair wind behind them, they sailed into the bay, hugging the Staten Island shore. Night was falling. They anchored, waiting for daylight.

The next day was bright and clear. Now they could plainly see the wooded heights of Staten Island, and opposite them the Long Island shore. And, gathered on that shore, an excited-looking crowd of Indians. They were beckoning and calling, with every sign of friendliness.

Young John was standing with his father at the rail. Robert Juet joined them.

"Do you see, sir?" he asked. "Those heathen are wearing some very fine fox skins. And I can see a gleam of ornaments—maybe it's gold." His greedy eyes glistened. "They want us to visit them. Will you let me take a boat and go, sir?"

"I think I shall go too," Hudson said thoughtfully.

John Hudson gave an excited gasp. "And me, Father?"

"Perhaps, Juet, order the longboat lowered. We'll not need more than six men—choose whomever you like. John, come into the cabin with me."

In the cabin, John helped his father fill a canvas bag with gifts. They were small trinkets, buttons and tin spoons and fishhooks, with a bone-handled knife for the chief. A small cask of brandy was put into the boat with the bag.

John watched anxiously as his father dressed himself for the visit. Out of the sea chest came the crimson velvet doublet, the long silk trunk hose, the snowy starched ruff. Carefully the Captain trimmed his beard to a sharp point and smoothed his thick dark hair, with its streaks of silver gray.

He turned from the tiny mirror to meet the boy's eyes.

"Smarten yourself up, boy," the father said kindly. "Captain Smith says these natives set great store by appearances. Yes, your Sunday suit by all means. It won't do for my son to show himself in shabby work-clothes."

John dressed in trembling haste, but he could not help asking a question.

"You didn't dress up for the first Indians we met, Father. And you didn't visit them, either."

Captain Hudson picked up his plumed hat. "I did not, and I see now that I was wrong," he admitted. "I should have remembered what Smith told me. It is important to win the friendship of these people. They can give us much useful information. It's true that we can't speak their language. But Juet managed very well with the sign language. I'm not very good at it myself. I want you to try your hand. And see if you can pick up some words in their tongue."

They came ashore somewhere near Coney Island, and John Hudson was the first white boy to see that fabulous place, which delights so many boys today. How amazed he would be if he could see Coney Island now! Then, it was a sandy spit of land on Gravesend Bay, with an

Indian fishing village the only sign of human life.

The Indians welcomed their visitors with joyous songs and dances. After the gifts were presented, a feast was spread. There were clams and oysters, broiled fish, and great heaped baskets of wild blueberries and grapes.

The feast grew even merrier when the brandy was passed around. It would have been wiser to leave the liquor aboard ship. The Indians would not have missed it. But after a few drinks, the natives became so friendly that they took off their fox skins and copper ornaments and pressed them upon their guests. Robert Juet at least took note of this for future reference.

It was late at night when the white men returned to the *Half Moon*. Captain Hudson was well pleased. The Indians had assured him that the bay was fed by a mighty stream of salt water. Salt water meant a strait; exactly what Hudson was looking for. The next day, he moved on.

The Coney Island landing was the only one that Hudson himself made in this region. He left the Indians his warm friends. It was a different story the next night.

They were now approaching the Narrows,

leading into the Upper Bay. The channel is deep enough to float the huge ocean liners which use it today. But Hudson could not know its depth. He anchored at the entrance, sending a boat ahead to take soundings.

The boat was in charge of John Colman, with four other men. They rowed slowly through the Narrows, testing the water's depth with a weighted line. Then, unexpectedly, they came into the wider reaches of the Upper Bay. Approaching the Manhattan side, they were delighted to find that the water continued deep right up to the shore.

The land itself enchanted them. It was, in their own words, "as pleasant with grasse and flowers and goodly trees as ever we had seene, and very sweet smells came from them." They did not go ashore, but turned back, toward sunset.

Darkness was falling as they approached the Narrows again. And out of the twilight, two Indian canoes came swiftly toward them. Before the white men knew what was happening, a rain of arrows flew through the autumn air. John Colman fell back, an arrow in his throat. And then, just as mysteriously as they had come, the Indians paddled quickly away.

There is no explanation for this attack. These were not the Indians that Hudson had visited, but a strange tribe from the New Jersey side. It is usual to say that all Indians were friendly until their trust was betrayed. But this was not always true. In Florida, for instance, the Spaniard Ponce de León was murdered by natives whose presence was not even known to him. Poor John Colman died for a reason that neither he nor any other white man was ever to know.

He was the only casualty. His crew, fearful of another attack, rowed about all night—a night of darkness and heavy rain. They could not find the entrance to the Narrows, and were afraid to go ashore. But the first morning light showed no sign of their attackers and they made their way back to the *Half Moon*. Colman was buried ashore, at a place they named Colman Point in his honor. Its location is unknown, but it was probably somewhere in South Brooklyn.

Hudson hoisted sail and moved on into the Upper Bay, following the route Colman had taken. In the evening they anchored at the spot we know now as the Battery, where the Hudson and the East River empty into the bay.

"Half Moon" on the Hudson

IN Battery Park, New York City, stands the statue of the first white man to enter New York Harbor. It is not a statue of Henry Hudson,

but of an almost forgotten Italian named Verrazano.

Giovanni da Verrazano, exploring for the
French, had arrived at this same point eighty-five
years before. He halted his ship at the Battery,
sending a boat ahead to explore. The boat was
rowed a mile or two upstream, to a point where
the river widens out. Verrazano's men took this
widening for a lake, and went no farther. The
Italian sailed away, leaving the river to the Indians.
His is the credit for the original discovery. But it
was Henry Hudson who opened the territory to
European settlement.

Captain Hudson did not linger long at the tip
of Manhattan Island. Moving steadily northward,
he anchored that night at Spuyten Duyvil. On the
following day, the *Half Moon* entered the majestic
mountain region of the Hudson Highlands. Even
Captain Hudson, who cared so little for the land,
was impressed by the wild mountain scenery.

He was impressed, too, by the friendliness of the
Indians who lived along the banks. At a point somewhere opposite where West Point now stands, he
made a state visit to a local chief. Again he was
received with song and feasting.

It was the suspicious Juet who marred the general good feeling. For no reason at all, he brought up the subject of Colman's murder, accusing their hosts of having committed it. The old chief, who had never heard of it, was completely bewildered. With stately gestures, he protested that he had never seen white men before, and certainly had not killed one.

"Don't believe him, sir," Juet whispered to his captain. "Oh, they're sly devils, these savages. No doubt he lured us here to kill us all. They'd like nothing better than to loot the ship and put us to the torture. Be on your guard, master, and keep your hand on your sword."

"I see no signs of such intention," Hudson answered. "To me they seem a peaceful, friendly people. I wish I could speak with them more freely, though."

"They'd only tell you lies if you could," Juet answered. "I tell you they're not to be trusted. Ah, you'd like to kill us this minute," he said to the chief. To make it clearer, he went through a pantomime of letting fly an arrow. Then, gasping, he fell back as though wounded.

His meaning was clear. The chief, with simple

dignity, took his own arrows from the quiver. Slowly he broke them with his hands and threw them into the fire.

Hudson, moved by the act, frowned at Juet. "I hope that shows you how wrong you were. Let's have no more such talk. If you cannot treat these people civilly, you may go back to the ship."

"As you say, sir," the man answered sulkily. "But you'll find out I'm right before we see the last of these murdering savages."

Juet's attitude was due to more than his natural taste for troublemaking. He wanted the furs and copper ornaments the Indians offered in trade. But he was a stingy man as well as a greedy one. Why give even trifles in exchange? And why let the Indians dole out their treasures, one by one, when you could have all of them by killing a few worthless heathens?

Once the natives could be provoked to attack, it would be easy to wipe them out with the white man's superior weapons. Of course, if Juet himself had been the Captain, he would not have had to wait for an attack. He would have come ashore with muskets blazing. But since Captain Hudson was so softhearted, it was necessary to make the Indians the aggressors.

He worked incessantly toward this end as the ship moved up the river. His friends among the crew were soon brought to share his views. Only Captain Hudson refused to do so.

One day, Juet brought the Captain a new scheme.

"You won't believe me when I say these savages aren't to be trusted, sir," he began. "But I have found a way to prove it. They are very fond of brandy. Let's invite a few chiefs aboard and get them drunk. When the liquor's in, the truth comes out, as is well known. Once their tongues are loosened, they'll give away their evil intentions."

Captain Hudson sighed. He had his own troubles, which did not concern the Indians. The mighty river was narrowing as they followed it north. And even more discouraging, the water was losing its salty taste. If the stream had been a strait connecting with the Pacific, it would be salt water all the way. But now it was almost fit for drinking. This might, after all, be only a river.

"Will you try it, sir?" Juet persisted. "It can do

no harm. And if what I suspect is true, it'll put you on your guard."

"Oh, try it if you like," Hudson answered. "The Indians have no reason to attack us. We are not taking their land. All we want is to find a passage through it. But have it your own way."

Gleefully, Juet issued the invitation at the next stopping place. A number of Indians were brought aboard, and plied with wine and brandy. They staggered about, laughed uproariously, and had a very gay time of it. One old man drank so much that he went to sleep and could not be roused until the next day, when the others had gone home. But no one revealed any sinister intentions. The old gentleman, waking without a headache, declared he had never been so happy in his life. Before the *Half Moon* sailed, he sent aboard a dressed deer, baskets of corn, and several strings of wampum to show his gratitude.

The ship came to a halt near the present location of Albany. The channel was now so shallow that it was risky to go farther. Hudson sent a boat ahead, in charge of the Dutch mate. The boat reached the present site of Waterford, and turned back. The great river had dwindled to a woodland stream no more than seven feet deep.

It was the end of Hudson's hopes. Once again he had tried for a new route to the Orient. Once again he had failed.

With a heavy heart, he gave the order to return downriver. Wrapped in gloom, he allowed the rascally Juet an even freer hand than usual. Juet made the most of it by stirring up trouble with the Indians. When the recent guests of the drinking party came again, Juet accused one of them of breaking into his cabin. He claimed the man had stolen a pillow, two shirts, and two knives.

This charge may or may not have been true. The Dutch mate, Juet's good friend, did not wait to find out. Catching up a musket, he shot the man dead.

The friendly visit broke up in the wildest confusion. The Indians took to their canoes in fright. One Indian steadied his canoe with a hand on the ship's boat. The cook chopped off the hand with a meat cleaver. Several sailors leaped into the boat, pursuing the fleeing Indians with bursts of gunfire.

Mr. Juet took no part in the pursuit. His own

hands, as he told the Captain virtuously, were clean of blood. He was the one who had been robbed, but he had not lifted a finger in return. Could he help it if his loyal friends had sought to avenge the wrong done him?

It had all happened so suddenly that the Captain had no way of knowing how it came about. As usual, he accepted Juet's explanation. When the boat returned, he ordered the men to set sail and hurry away down the river.

There was another battle a day or so later, when a canoe party sought to visit the ship. Juet claimed that these were the same Indians—even that he recognized his shirt on one of them. Without waiting for the Captain's permission, he ordered the ship's cannon fired. The Indians responded with a flight of arrows. Another cannon-burst put them to flight, with the aid of a few musket-shots.

The *Half Moon* sailed on, and anchored on the New Jersey shore near Hoboken. Juet thought he saw a copper or silver mine there, and wanted to explore it. But Captain Hudson had had enough of this river. As soon as daylight came, he ordered all sails set. Two days later they were clear of New York Bay, heading out into the Atlantic.

Since they were on the American side of the ocean, the Captain's thoughts turned again to the Furious Overfall. In talking to Smith, he had spoken of trying both routes on one voyage. He could see for himself now how impossible that was. Winter was coming on. The northern waters would be solidly frozen. The Furious Overfall would have to wait for a new expedition in the spring. There was nothing to do but go home and try again.

And so ended the voyage which was to make Henry Hudson's name immortal. However disappointed he may have been, he had served his employers well. For the Dutch he had found a kingdom, many times larger than the parent country, a kingdom rich in furs and minerals and in thousands of acres of fertile farmland. The Dutch received very good value for the $208 they paid Captain Hudson.

The Last Voyage

CAPTAIN HUDSON had learned by experience how hard it was to get a ship for exploration. He had a ship in his possession now. On
the way home from America, he thought of a
simple scheme to keep it for the next voyage.

He did not return to Holland. Instead, he took
the *Half Moon* into Dartmouth, an English port.
From there he sent to the Dutch company a full

account of the expedition, and of the territory he had gained for their country. With their permission, he added, he would winter in England and leave in early spring to seek a route through the Furious Overfall.

It was a bold move which might have succeeded. But before the Dutch could reply, the English took a hand. News of Hudson's discoveries excited interest in his own country. If an Englishman were to make discoveries of this sort, they should be made for England. King James issued an order forbidding Hudson to continue in Dutch service. And without being coaxed, a group of prominent Englishmen offered to raise the money for a new voyage.

This suited Hudson very well. He sent the *Half Moon* home in charge of the Dutch crew, and gladly turned his attention to outfitting the English ship offered him. His principal backers were three wealthy merchants, Sir Thomas Smith, John Wolstenholme, and Sir Dudley Digges. They furnished a stout little bark, the *Discovery*.

The noble patrons were more generous in money matters than the Dutch. Not so satisfactory, however, was their interference in the matter of the crew. Juet, who was to be first mate, was not allowed to choose all the men. The backers had a few hangers-on who wanted to go. These men were not sailors. One, Abacuk Prickett, was Sir Dudley's footman. Edward Wilson was a drunken young surgeon who had lost too many patients. There was another Wilson, called Bill, in trouble with the police. The worst of the lot, however, was a black sheep of respectable parents who wanted him out of England. Hudson himself had been persuaded to take this Henry Greene along to make a new start.

With these men, and with those Juet gathered around him, Hudson could scarcely have had a worse crew. As always, he gave little attention to the character of his men. They were there to sail the ship. So long as the ship sailed on, the Captain was not concerned about them.

There were a few good men among them. Philip Staffe, the honest carpenter, could be counted upon for faithful service. So could the ship's gunner, John Williams. One of the patrons had sponsored Thomas Wydowse, a young mathematician with a taste for adventure. Wydowse alone had the education to understand the Captain's plans.

He became his close friend. There was also, of course, young John Hudson.

The *Discovery* sailed from London on April 17, 1610. Proceeding by way of Iceland and Greenland, they reached the American coast in late summer. They spent some time ranging up and down in search of the Furious Overfall. This is the neck of water now called Hudson Strait. They found it, or its mouth, toward the middle of August.

The Furious Overfall was not so furious as the early descriptions. There was plenty of ice. But the channel was wide, and the steersman could always manage to dodge the floating cakes. Even the strong current, although it made progress difficult, slowed them but did not stop them. Pressing steadily onward, they came at last to the vast inland sea we know as Hudson Bay.

Could this be the Pacific Ocean? It seemed too good to be true. And yet, what else could it be?

Hudson summoned his son and the student Wydowse to his cabin. His voice trembling with eagerness, he explained his plans.

"We'll need to turn southwestward now," he said. "But not too far south. That would bring us to India, where the Dutch are already trading. What we want to aim for is China, and perhaps the Japanese islands. No European power has a foothold in those mysterious lands. That's the place for us."

"Will we conquer them for England," John asked, "as the Spanish did the Indian kingdoms in South America and Mexico?"

"We will not," Hudson answered. "Our employers are sending us out for trade, not conquest. Of course, we'll report what we find when we return home. If our lord the King chooses to send warships and armies to win these lands, that is his business. It is not ours."

John looked a little disappointed, but soon cheered up.

"Anyway, we'll go back with a fine cargo of silks and pearls and spices. And you've been promised a share in the profits, haven't you, Father? It'll make you a rich man. You can buy your own ship next time, without having to ask anyone."

"Perhaps," Captain Hudson said absently. "John, I'd like you to launder my best shirts, and my neck ruffs. Your own, too. We must look our best when we call upon the Emperor of China."

Sure though he was that he had reached the Pacific, Hudson had no way of guessing how far it might be to China. It was infuriating that ice and fog held them to a slow crawl. They had learned now to make fast to an ice floe when the weather was against them, waiting as patiently as possible until they could move on again.

The men, at least, had expected to find China within a few days. But the days passed, and still they inched their way through ice, or waited for the frequent fogs to lift. A week of this, and the men began to grumble.

Robert Juet, as always, was behind the discontent. Talking to the sailors, he made fun of the Captain's hopes. How, he asked them, were they better off in this ocean than in the Atlantic? It was just as cold here, and the ice was just as fierce. Frostbite was just as painful. They were all sick of the unending battle against ice and cold. If *he* were captain, Juet declared, he would turn the ship about and go home. And then—more boldly—perhaps he would do it anyway, if the men would back him.

It happened that Mr. Juet failed to make sure that he was not overheard by the loyal seamen.

One of them reported his rash talk to the Captain.

This was the point at which Captain Hudson would have done well to rid himself of his vicious enemy. If he could not bring himself to hang him, he could have had him put in irons. Instead, he acted with the fairness and decency which marked all his acts.

The entire crew was summoned to an inquiry. Several men testified to what they had heard. Even Juet's old friend Arnold Lodlo admitted that Juet had told him to keep his musket handy, "in case the Captain makes trouble when I take over."

Juet indignantly denied it all. He had had a falling out with Lodlo, who was trying to get even. This is likely enough. But, in his spite, Lodlo was telling the truth.

The majority supported Juet's denials. Hudson did not know what to think. In the end, he let Juet off with a stern reprimand, replacing him as mate by a man named Bylot.

The inquiry had proved useful to the villain. Now he knew which men were his friends, and which ones were against him. One of his strongest supporters was the rogue Henry Greene. Juet took him into partnership in the business of making

trouble for the Captain. Greene proved even more gifted in that line than Juet himself.

The belief that Hudson Bay was the Pacific Ocean died hard. But the southwestward course brought them to bleak Arctic land which no one could mistake for the Flowery Kingdom. Hopefully, Hudson turned back and set another course. West and north he ranged, seeking for a clear passage. Sometimes he thought he had found one, between an island and a cape. But always, once the island was passed, he came up against land again.

Three weary months went by, and still they were sailing around in a great watery pocket. There must be a way out of it. Hudson was sure of that. But the nights were growing longer, the ice more solid. The terrible Arctic winter was upon them.

Even Captain Hudson, impatient though he was, had to admit that they could not go on until spring. Postponement was maddening, with their goal so near. But there was no help for it. They chose a sheltered spot, a smaller bay at the southern tip of the great one. It is now called James Bay, for a later explorer. Here, hauled close to shore, the *Discovery* was frozen in for the winter.

The months that followed were wretched ones. The ship had provisions for six months. But food would be needed when they resumed the voyage. Hudson divided the stock and locked half of it in a chest in his cabin. Henry Greene declared the Captain and his son dipped into it to feed themselves.

The ship's bread grew moldy and the salt meat spoiled. At first, the men were able to help out by shooting wild fowl and catching fish. But as the iron cold of the winter set in, the birds fled south and were seen no more. The ice in the bay turned solid, too thick for breaking a hole to fish through.

There was nothing to do, nowhere to go, nothing but darkness and cold and illness. Most of the men suffered from scurvy, caused by lack of fresh food. This is a most distressing disease. The joints swell, turning strong men into cripples. Gums turn black, teeth fall out, and extreme weakness sets in. Scurvy is easily, almost magically, cured by the vitamin-bearing fruits and vegetables. But these the *Discovery's* crew did not have.

It is not strange that tempers grew short, and incessant quarreling broke out. Even Captain Hudson's calm disposition changed for the worse. Early in the winter, the ship's gunner died of pneumonia. This man, Williams, owned a very thick, warm cloak. Henry Greene claimed that the dying man had promised it to him. But Hudson gave it to another man, who seemed in greater need. He rebuked Greene angrily when he protested. If Greene had needed anything to add to his hatred of the Captain, he had it now.

Somehow the endless winter came to an end. The days grew longer. The ice, which had held the ship fast, began to melt. Green tips appeared on the stunted evergreen trees ashore. Young Wydowse boiled these twigs into tea, recommending it for the scurvy sufferers. Those who tried it did get some relief. Most of them rejected it because of its bitter taste. However, mosses gathered from under the melting snow served the same purpose. All the men recovered except some half-dozen, who continued ill for the rest of the voyage.

Little by little, the ice relaxed its grip on the ship. On a bright June day, the *Discovery* left its winter moorings in James Bay. They headed due north, to where the smaller bay emptied into the larger one. They knew now that Hudson Bay was not the Pacific Ocean. But Captain Hudson never wavered in his firm belief that the ocean lay just beyond, and that he would surely find his way to it.

The Mutiny

PROGRESS out of the winter haven was slow. They were not yet clear of James Bay on the night of June 21, 1611.

For what happened on that dreadful night, we have only the report of Abacuk Prickett, footman to one of the backers. Prickett was a weak, well-meaning fellow, chiefly interested in saving his own skin. His account may not be entirely truthful, but the main facts as he told them seem likely enough.

Prickett was one of those who had never recovered from the hardships of the winter. There were four others, totally disabled and unable to leave their bunks. Prickett himself had badly swollen knees and frostbitten feet. The pain was so intense that he slept little, spending his time reading his Bible. He was so engaged when Henry Greene and Bill Wilson entered his cubbyhole.

In husky whispers they told Prickett their plan. The Captain was determined to continue on this mad quest for an opening into the Pacific. Only that day, he had announced that the far northwestern corner had not yet been explored. As soon as the wind was right, he meant to set a course in that direction.

Greene and Wilson did not know or care whether there was an opening there. They were sure of only one opening out of this watery trap, and that was the one by which they had entered.

The Furious Overfall lay to the eastward. Beyond it was the open Atlantic. And beyond that, the dear land of England. No more ice, no more suffering, no more starvation. Home, and their families, and everything that made life sweet.

"We have made up our minds," Greene told Prickett. "The master will not listen to reason. He is a lunatic, ready to throw away his own life and ours with it. We are taking the ship out of his hands. We are going home."

"But he is the captain," Prickett protested. "He will never consent."

"He won't be asked," Wilson put in. "We're going to put him into the shallop and turn him adrift."

"The shallop?" Prickett looked puzzled for a minute. He was a landsman who had never bothered to learn sailor-talk. "Oh, the ship's boat, you mean. But this is a wicked thing! To turn him out alone—"

"He won't be alone," Wilson said with a coarse laugh. "We'll give him the sick men for company. They're lying in their bunks, eating their share, and doing no work for it. We'll be better off without them."

Now Prickett started up in alarm. He was one of the sick men. But Greene quickly reassured him.

"Oh, not you. We'll need you to explain when

we get home. Robert Juet says he can tell the story so we won't be blamed. But your word carries weight with Sir Dudley Digges. You and Juet must make out the tale of the Captain's cruelties. It's a true tale, as well you know. But it must be well told. Now, Master Prickett, what do you say?"

"I say it's a wicked, disgraceful deed," Prickett answered. "I'll have no part in it."

"As you like," Greene said calmly. "But perhaps you'll be sorry when you find yourself in the shallop."

They left him then, to think it over. When they came back an hour later, Prickett had found a way to soothe his conscience.

He offered them his open Bible, demanding that they repeat after him: "I swear truth to God, my prince and my country; I shall do nothing but to the glory of God and the good of the action in hand, and harm to no man."

Exactly what this oath meant, or what good it could do, is hard to understand. It satisfied Prickett. Greene and Wilson took the oath on the spot. Then they sent in five other men, including Robert Juet. All of them swore as Prickett directed. They left him with his Bible, in which he had found the consoling text: "There are many devices in the heart of man, but the counsel of the Lord shall stand."

Out on deck, the conspirators gathered for the next move. It may be noticed that Greene and Wilson took the lead. Juet was content to have it so. If the scheme failed, he could assure the Captain that he had had no part in it. If it succeeded, he could tell the owners that the men had called upon him to take charge. There is no doubt, of course, that he was in the plot heart and soul.

After a brief final talk, they scattered to their places. Bill Wilson and a sailor named Thomas hid themselves near Hudson's cabin door. Just opposite it, John Hudson was sharing a tiny cabin with the drunken doctor. The carpenter, Philip Staffe, was sleeping on the poop deck. Greene and another man went to stand over him. Juet made himself responsible for John King, known to be loyal to the Captain.

No one made a move until dawn began to break. Then the quiet was shattered by the cook clattering his kettle as he crossed the deck to the water barrel. The cheerful familiar noise wakened Captain Hudson, as it always did. He could not know that this time it was the signal agreed upon by the plotters.

The Captain dressed hastily and stepped outdoors to have a look at the new day. Would wind and weather be right for moving on? The *Discovery* had been moored here to an ice floe for a week. But perhaps this was the day that the luck would change.

Quietly the cook set his kettle down. He joined Bill Wilson and John Thomas in their hiding-place near the doorway. Hudson, his eyes scanning the horizon, did not hear the stealthy approach. He was taken completely by surprise when the three men suddenly sprang upon him. Thomas and the cook held his arms while Wilson, from behind, bound him tightly with rope.

"What is the meaning of this?" the Captain gasped.

"You'll know when you're in the shallop," Wilson retorted. "This way, men. Bring him along."

The cabin door opposite flew open. The doctor stuck his head out. Behind him could be seen the frightened face of young John Hudson.

"What is happening?" the doctor shouted. Bill Wilson turned to face him.

"Are you well, Master Surgeon?" he inquired.

"Well? Why, yes, I am well. But what—"

"Then see that you keep yourself so," Wilson snarled.

The doctor needed no further hint. Without another word, he went back to bed, and stayed there.

John Hudson, terrified though he was, knew no place except at his father's side. Trembling and silent, he joined the Captain, reaching in vain for his bound hand.

The boy had not figured in the plan. Wilson turned to Greene, who had just arrived. "The cub, too?" he asked.

"Certainly," Greene replied. "Heaven knows what tales he would tell if we took him back to England. Tie him up and bring him with the old man."

Things moved swiftly after that. Hudson and John were lowered into the boat. Then came the four sick men. Hudson's friend Wydowse followed. These were to have been the only victims. But there was another, by his own choice.

This was the carpenter, Philip Staffe. He was a useful man aboard ship, too useful to lose. The

plotters had not tried to involve him, knowing his devotion to the Captain. But he was slow-thinking and easygoing. Probably they counted on his remaining in ignorance until it was too late to interfere.

To his bewildered inquiries, Greene replied that it was nothing to do with him. All he had to do was to hold his hand now, and to hold his tongue later. Soon he would be on the way home. And even sooner, he would be sitting down to a good meal. The Captain's hoarded food was to be shared among the crew without delay.

The simple carpenter answered them in simple words.

"I will sooner die with the master than live with such villains as you. Give me my chest of tools, and I will go down into the shallop."

Perhaps the noble words shamed their black hearts. When they lowered him into the boat, they gave him, not only his tools, but his musket, some meal, and an iron pot.

The foul deed was done now, except for the final stroke. The cook took his cleaver and chopped away the tow rope. Slowly the gap of green water widened between the *Discovery* and its frail little rowboat.

The mutineers did not wait to see it drift out of sight. They were too busy looting the ship. First the hoarded food, a scanty supply of meal, butter, salt pork, and a cask of beer. But there were other treasures. Clothes, bedding, the Captain's personal belongings, Wydowse's books, which they could not read. Prickett, lying snug in bed, comments that they behaved like soldiers looting a city. Dr. Wilson, once it was all over, got up and took a hand in the looting.

That same day, with a favorable wind, the *Discovery* sailed out of James Bay and turned toward the Furious Overfall and the Atlantic.

It was not a happy voyage. Juet, who had expected to take command, found himself in dispute with Greene. Juet wanted to go back to England and collect a reward for saving the ship for its owners. Greene, on the other hand, had decided it would be more profitable to turn pirate and sail south to plunder the Spanish treasure ships.

Neither plan came to anything. At the mouth of Hudson Strait they saw some Eskimo huts.

They went ashore in search of food, and found themselves in a battle with the Eskimos. Bill Wilson and John Thomas were killed by spears. Henry Greene died a little later of an arrow-shot.

Juet and the cook, with several others, had remained aboard ship. They hoisted sail and fled for the open sea. They were practically out of food. After they had shot and eaten a few birds, the villainous cook had to invent a new recipe. He pounded up the bird bones, fried them in candle grease, and seasoned them with vinegar.

This may have been the last meal that Robert Juet ever ate. He died a little later of starvation. So did some others. The *Discovery*, after many hardships, finally reached England. Abacuk Prickett and Dr. Edward Wilson were among the survivors. With some of the men, they were tried for mutiny. They were acquitted when they convinced the court that they had been innocent bystanders. The ringleaders were already dead, so no one was ever punished for the unspeakable crime.

And what of the shallop? There is no way of knowing what happened to it. All we know of Henry Hudson's last hours aboard ship comes from Prickett's account. And Prickett was far more interested in proving his own innocence than in reporting the Captain's words or deeds. How Hudson felt, what he thought or said or did, no one now can ever know. From all we know of the man, and of his devoted young son, we can feel sure that they met their fate bravely, whatever that fate may have been.

It may well be that Captain Henry Hudson found his last resting place beneath the waters of the bay which bears his name. However, there is one possible ending which is a bit more cheerful. They were not far from land, where scrub trees grew. They had a skilled carpenter on board, with his tools.

Did they reach land? Did Staffe build them a house? Once sure of shelter, they could have fished, and shot wild game with Staffe's musket. It would have been a rugged life, but not an impossible one. For all we know, they may have lived out their days in peace.

There is just one tiny shred of evidence to support this hopeful view. Sixty years later, the French trapper Pierre Radisson explored Hudson Bay. Somewhere on the shore, not too far from where the shallop was set adrift, Radisson found the ruins of a wooden house. It was English built, as the Frenchman could tell by the marks of tools unknown to the Eskimos. It was just such a house as Philip Staffe might have built.

Perhaps he did build it. Perhaps the little party lived out their lives in the Canadian wilderness, and died there. Sixty years is a long time. Even John, the youngest of them, could hardly have survived to the time of Radisson's visit.

We shall never know. Henry Hudson's life ended, soon or late, as all men's lives must end. It is not his death, but his life, for which his name is remembered. And while the Hudson River flows, while the world's proudest city stands where he saw only "goodly trees" and sweet-smelling flowers, that name will never be forgotten.

Authorities Consulted

BOOKS

BACON, EDGAR MAYHEW. *Henry Hudson, his times and his voyages.* New York: G. P. Putnam's Sons, 1907

HALL, EDWARD H. "Henry Hudson and the Discovery of the Hudson River." In *American Scenic and Historic Preservation Society, annual report.* Albany, 1910

JANVIER, THOMAS A. *Henry Hudson.* New York: Harper and Brothers, 1909

MURPHY, HENRY C. *Henry Hudson in Holland.* The Hague: Martinus Nijhoff, 1909

POWYS, LLEWELYN. *Henry Hudson.* New York: Harper and Brothers, 1928

SCOTT, J. M. *Hudson of Hudson's Bay.* New York: Henry Schuman, 1951

ENCYCLOPÆDIA BRITANNICA (14th edition). 24 vols. Chicago: Encyclopædia Britannica, Incorporated, 1954

AUTHORITIES CONSULTED

MAGAZINES

Harper's Weekly, September 25, 1909
National Geographic, April, 1939
Review of Reviews, October, 1909
Scientific American, September 25, 1909

Index

Index

Index

About the Author

NINA BROWN BAKER was born in Galena, Kansas, and lived in several mid-western cities after her marriage to Sidney J. Baker. In 1938 she and her husband migrated to New York, and Mrs. Baker began to write her popular biographies for young people. For several years before her sudden death in 1957, this well-loved author had made her home on Brooklyn Heights.

As a young girl, Mrs. Baker taught in a rural school in Colorado and rode to and from her classroom on horseback. This experience, plus the happy years spent in raising her own two daughters, may partly explain her gift for bringing famous characters from history to life for younger readers. Mrs. Baker believed that the most interesting way to learn about a country is through the lives of its great men because, as she herself said, "that way you get a good story too."

Mrs. Baker has left over twenty biographies for boys and girls—among them *Juarez, Hero of Mexico, Pike of Pike's Peak, Nickels and Dimes, Boy for a Man's Job, Amerigo Vespucci, Juan Ponce de Leon,* and *Henry Hudson.* Her death is a great loss to the field of children's books.

A NOTE ON THE

Type

IN WHICH THIS BOOK IS SET

THE TEXT *of this book was set on the Linotype in Janson, a recutting made direct from type cast from the original matrices cut by Anton Janson. Janson, who may have been of Dutch origin, purchased a foundry and was a practicing type-founder in Leipzig between 1660 and 1687. His first specimen sheet was issued in 1675. His successor, Johann Karl Edling, issued a later specimen sheet showing all of Janson's types in 1689. The Janson matrices were later brought to Holland, from whence they were sold in 1720 to the Erhardt foundry of Leipzig. Later acquired by the Drugulin foundry of Leipzig, they eventually passed into the hands of the Schriftgiesserei Stempel of Frankfurt am Main, where they are now preserved.*

Janson is an excellent example of the sturdy and influential Dutch old style types that prevailed throughout Europe during the seventeenth and early eighteenth centuries. It is highly legible, and its individual letters have a pleasing variety of design.

COMPOSED, printed, and bound by H. Wolff, New York. Paper manufactured by P. H. Glatfelter, Co., Spring Grove, Pa. Typography by Charles Farrell.

NORTH AMERICA

HUDSON BAY

Hudson River

FIRST VOYAGE
SECOND VOYAGE
THIRD VOYAGE
FOURTH VOYAGE